"Karen Scott Barss has expressed, with great depth of insight and spiritual sensitivity, the journey of a person coping with a life-threatening illness. In so doing, she has provided a valuable resource for those who find themselves in a similar circumstance, their significant others, professional health caregivers and educators. *Healing Images* is also a timely and valuable contribution to current efforts within healthcare to care for the whole person."

- Rev. Don Misener, D.Min
Spiritual Care Educator, St. Paul's Hospital, Saskatoon, Sask. Can.

"Karen has written a powerful account of her personal confrontation with a life-threatening illness and her continuing journey to healing. Although many people would have kept such an account private, Karen has shared generously from her experience. In so doing, she has produced a book which expresses common experiences of human hurt and healing with sensitivity, compassion and humility. This book will be a source of comfort and hope for anyone who is dealing with a serious personal trauma. This book will also be a source of guidance and deeper understanding for professional caregivers."

- Dr. Anne Doig, Family Physician and ^
Obstetrics and Gynecology

"Personal stories have always been a source of wisdom for others. As I read *Healing Images* my whole being was affected. My head comprehended the struggles and challenges Karen dealt with. My heart empathized with her feelings of chaos, shock, anger and vulnerability at receiving the diagnosis of breast cancer. My strongest response to the poetry was a spiritual one. The poems were 'soul food' and resonated deep within me. The poetry spoke truth and wisdom while at the same time validated the depth of feelings I had experienced when coping with significant losses in my own life.

I see this poetry as a valuable tool for self-understanding and enhancing communication with family members. It offers us words and descriptions when our own voice fails. Having someone else's experience to relate to offers us a sense of connection and relatedness. To know we are not alone offers comfort. *Healing Images* offers readers courage and hope, and a story of transformation into personal healing."

- Moira Theede, BSN, MSc, Healing Touch Practitioner

Healing

REFLECTIONS ON A HEALING JOURNEY

Images

Karen Scott Barss

Illustrations by Shauna Barss

The Granny Ranch Publishing House™

Books are available at special discounts on bulk orders for book stores, fundraising or educational use.

Illustrations: Shauna Barss ©1999

Cover photograph: Courtney Milne

Cover design: Ed Pas

Layout: Karen Barss and Lucille Stewart

'The Granny Ranch' logo design: Allan Barss ©1999

ISBN: 1-896971-01-6

*CIP Data:
1. Barss, Karen Scott, 1961-
2. Breast — Cancer — Patients — Saskatchewan — Biography
3. Healing.
RC280.B8 B27 1999   362.1'9699449'0092   C99-920042-9*

*Printed by St. Peter's Press
Box 190
Muenster, SK Canada S0K 2Y0*

*Published by The Granny Ranch Publishing House
Box 23026 - 2325 Preston Avenue
Saskatoon, SK Canada S7J 5H3
Email: kms.barss@sk.sympatico.ca*

The Granny Ranch is a place of healing that promotes and celebrates longevity, femininity, growth and wisdom.

Dedication

To my beloved, our two precious sons

and all the others who have walked lovingly

beside me on this journey.

Without you, I would be much further back

on the way of healing.

Foreword

My heroes are ordinary people who do extra-ordinary things. Karen Scott Barss is one of those people. *Healing Images: Reflections on a Healing Journey* is an extra-ordinary thing. It is a book about hope and healing. It encourages us to believe in ourselves and believe in the possibility of transformation. This book is a valuable map for those embarking on a healing journey and a helpful guide for those already on their path. Karen is a healer by profession and so has the opportunity to give a perspective of a 'wounded healer'. Each wound we suffer and eventually heal from becomes an opportunity for transformation, spiritual growth and healing.

There is great healing in the sharing of stories. The ability to tell our stories is positively linked with recovery. Those on a healing journey search for meaning in the experience in order to gain mastery over the event. Viktor Frankel says in his book, *Man's Search for Meaning*, "Our main concern is not to gain pleasure or to avoid pain, but rather to see a meaning in one's life." By finding her voice and telling her stories, Karen is able to give meaning to her experiences. We find healing for ourselves through these shared stories. We help to heal one another when we have the courage to tell our stories.

Karen is a fellow breast cancer survivor. The first time I read *Healing Images*, I was reminded of the losses in my life. I grieved again, relived my own story and moved further along on my healing journey. In spite of these memories hope was always within reach. Grace and wisdom are found on every page of *Healing Images*, hope wins over despair, triumph wins over tragedy.

Healing ourselves, we heal our communities, we begin to heal our world. A cancer diagnosis is not a time for complacency, it is a time for reflection and a time for healing. Cancer is a life-changing experience that, when closely examined, provides opportunities for positive change.

Suffering can be a doorway to transformation, as Karen demonstrates through her imagery, meditations, poetry and prose. I am reminded of the transformation of the caterpillar through the cocoon phase to the glorious butterfly. I was recently blessed with the opportunity to watch a caterpillar spin a cocoon, then doubly blessed to see the butterfly emerge three weeks later. The mystery of this transformation parallels the miracle of life itself ... the mystery out of which we are born and to which we return. To live in this great mystery means to sometimes live with fear and uncertainty, but mostly it means to live with awe, wonder and hope. When we are in transition we are vulnerable. When we take care of ourselves we become agents of our own transformation.

We all need to see that our life has meaning, we need to know that somebody cares and we need to maintain a high level of hope and joy. Karen Scott Barss truly lives her beliefs. I applaud her courage, her compassion and her grace. She has come through the wilderness to the light of hope, love and joy. *Healing Images: Reflections on a Healing Journey* is an extra-ordinary book.

Catherine Ripplinger Fenwick
Author, *Healing With Humour* and *Telling My Sister's Story*
Regina, Saskatchewan

Contents

Acknowledgments

I have been richly blessed to cross paths with so many who have generously contributed their support, inspiration and unique gifts to the creative process that has brought *Healing Images* to reality. To each and every one of you I extend a heartfelt and humble 'Thank You'.

Specifically, I would like to honour first and foremost, my husband, Barry, who has been my anchor and my strength in countless tangible and intangible ways as I have been immersed in this endeavor. In doing so, he has taught much to our two sons, Trevor & Ian. They display on a daily basis his qualities of steadiness, patience and unconditional acceptance of the dreams and challenges associated with the creation and sharing of *Healing Images*. Their ongoing excitement and encouragement has been a precious gift.

A world of gratitude also goes to my parents, Hartley and Marion Scott and my parents-in-law, Don & Donna Barss for their unwavering support and ready assistance with many tasks. To all of my siblings and 'sibs-in-law', thanks for believing in and supporting me in this offering. There are many, many other close ones in our extended family and circle of friends whose involvement and support also has been pivotal.

A very special thank you goes to ...

... Saskatchewan Blue Cross for their financial support and encouragement

... Courtney Milne and Sherrill Miller for the beautiful cover photograph - truly a healing image! (More Courtney Milne images may be seen at www.CourtneyMilne.com)

... Ed Pas for the marvelous cover design - another gift from the universe!

... Cathy Fenwick for the affirmation of her Foreword, mentorship and guidance

... Shauna Barss for her beautifully and sensitively interpreted illustrations (more healing images!)

... Allan & Colleen Barss for the inspired 'Granny Ranch' logo

... Kevin Scott for his generously-offered and thorough legal advice

... Ruth Savage for her 'eagle-eye editing' and insightful feedback

... Dr. Dennis Kendel, Rev. Don Misener, Dr. Anne Doig, Dr. Gerri Dickson, Sherrill Miller, Courtney Milne, Moira Theede, Denean Hall, Marilyn Robinson, Marie Thomas, Sherry McDonald, Sandra Church, Dr. Esther Stenberg and Dr. Gary Groot for their validation and contributions

... HOPE Saskatoon and Breast Cancer Action Saskatchewan (BCAS) for their practical and moral support

... writers Harry Rintouil and Bill Robertson for their guidance and feedback

... Diana Davidson Dyck and Lois Berry of SIAST for facilitating a leave of absence from my teaching position to complete this offering

... Anne Elliott and Patricia Smith at Spiritworks Gifts, Books & Music, Saskatoon for their validation and support

... Corie Hetzel and Lucille Stewart at St. Peter's Press for their conscientious and creative work

... my friends in the Registered Psychiatric Nursing (RPN), breast cancer support, health care, nursing education & United Church communities who have taught me, loved me and learned with me.

All of these people and their Gifts are ongoing affirmations of Spirit's Presence on our path.

Introduction

I had been told more than once I should write a book about my experience
with breast cancer and the ensuing journey on which my close ones and I
found ourselves. I'm not sure if people gave me this encouragement because
they thought I had something to offer or because they were aware of my
tendency to expound upon my feelings, experiences and insights with those
I trust - to "blab on and on" as my sons indelicately put it! In any case, my
initial response to such comments was to think "What do *I* have to say to
others who have to face the terrors of such a crisis that they aren't going to
figure out on their own? - because they *have* to!"

This sense was initially reinforced by my subsequent personal involvement
with many other people living with serious illness and significant life
challenges. Indeed, there were incredible commonalities amongst our
experiences. Through sharing these experiences, I found powerful validation
for my own reactions. I also accessed invaluable learning about how I could
heal from the trauma of the experience. Much of this learning was gained
from people experiencing greater challenges and far less support than I. Still
more of it was gained from people at a place much further down the way of
healing than I could even envision at the time. What did *I* possibly have to
say?

As time went on, it became apparent that, perhaps, I did have something to
offer in return. Within the relationships I experienced, I discovered it is *not* a
given we will figure things out on our own; we *need* each other's support and
insight. Perhaps, I just *rediscovered* on a deeper, personal level what I had
always known. My work as a Registered Psychiatric Nurse and educator had
allowed me to witness the pain of others who were not only traumatized by
illness, abuse or loss but were dramatically debilitated by an ongoing lack of
support and validation for their pain. Still, the gifts I had to offer were no
different than those offered to me. What was different, perhaps, was the *way*
in which I could share them.

Ideas for poetic reflections began to arise out of the scribbled pages of journaling I had started to write each morning. For a long time, I would simply scrawl these ideas in the margins; I was still too heartsick to be able to create them. Finally, I was prompted to let the ideas take shape one morning when I had forgotten to take my journal on an over-night trip. To fill the void in my morning routine, I took pen and fresh paper in hand. The beginnings of "Sailing Out" appeared. The rest of the amazing process that unfolded is best told by the poem appearing second in the collection, "Voice". The poetry has been both a source and a result of healing ever since.

As the poetry evolved into this book, I added a prosaic reflection to accompany each poetic one that had surfaced. As I reflected on each set of reflections and the lesson that seemed to be at their core, I wrote a short affirmation to help internalize positive messages I so very much need to carry within as I navigate the ongoing and difficult journey of healing. Perhaps these affirmations can serve as a springboard for you, the reader, to begin to create your own affirmations - ones that are the most powerful for you and the challenges you face.

In any case, this blending of poetry, prose and affirmation has given me a powerful and unique way to find healing. It has also given me a way to express much in a very concise format, perhaps serving as a medium to support others and to enhance awareness of the experience of healing. I believe that Spirit guided this process with a wisdom that knows lengthy accounts are the last thing most of us feel like reading when we're sick, tired and overwhelmed. I know such accounts were the last things I felt like writing! (Much to my sons' surprise, I'm sure!)

My hope is that you will experience this book in a way that assists you to begin to tell *your* story. I believe it is critical that no assumptions be made that your experiences are the same as mine - particularly if you have experienced significantly different hurts. In fact, I initially envisioned the book focusing only around breast cancer experiences; while I knew that much of what I struggled with was universal to all healing, I wanted to stay clear of assumptions about my ability to speak to other traumas. Colleagues and other close ones with whom I shared the beginnings of this book convinced me that there was, indeed, a wider audience who might benefit from the sharing of my experience. I thank all who provided me with invaluable insights into what this book was meant to be - a book about finding healing. If sharing my story helps readers to find voice for theirs, I am humbled and delighted; I believe finding voice for our story is central to healing for all of us. I don't even want to imagine where I would be if all of the things I have been able to express here were still caught somewhere inside me.

While the reflections appeared to me in a very random order, they appear here in a progression that roughly reflects my own healing journey. This progression has been visible to me only in retrospect. You may find it helpful to follow this progression as you read, so you can be witness to a process of transition that has been occurring over a significant period of time with a significant amount of energy and support. On the other hand, it may be helpful for you to hop around from page to page, reading what speaks to you on a given day.

Of course, there are as many ways to experience this book as there are people reading it. Whether you use it for comfort, meditation, journaling, discussion, to share with close ones, or to enhance understanding of the healing process - I hope it assists you and those important to you to find *your* Healing Images.

* * * * * * *

My Mom did a wonderful job of fostering my imagination as a child. Many hours were spent together reading books full of vivid imagery. Neither of us knew at the time that my ability to readily visualize life's intangible elements would become much more than an enjoyable pastime - it has been my *lifeline* throughout my first personal encounter with trauma, a diagnosis of breast cancer followed by a mastectomy, chemotherapy and other measures. Frequently, I have used symbolic mental images to maintain a positive outlook, reduce fear, cope with medical interventions, and promote healing. Who would have thought an imagination could be so practical?!

I coupled this use of imagination with my Dad's beloved and familiar adage of "Live and Learn". I was determined to honour this message and to try to mirror my Dad's remarkable ability to accept and learn from life's painful experiences. I was to find out how very difficult a task this is. Still, this approach allowed me to be comfortable with accessing many resources and experiences to help me expand upon my ability to use imagery for healing and general well-being. I also relied heavily on the solid spiritual base which both my parents had fostered.

Thus, I was more prepared to handle adversity than I ever could have been without these gifts from my parents. While nothing can prepare one to cope with the terror of a life-threatening illness, their gifts anchored me as I was tossed about on the waves of a totally foreign experience.

My Imagination is no frill.
It is a powerful catalyst for healing, change and growth.

Healing Images

Healing images
In my mind
Bring health to all of me.
They fill my body
And my soul
With creativity.

Healing images
Show me all
I can become in time.
They bring God close
So I can see
A brighter paradigm.

Healing images
Guide me through
Dark days that seem to come.
They hold me up
And give reserve
To draw my courage from.

Healing images
Fill my life
With things that matter most.
They help me know
I have a Guide -
An unseen Holy Host.

For a considerable time following cancer treatment I was unable to articulate even to myself the overwhelming devastation and confusion I felt in response to a diagnosis of breast cancer. I couldn't even journal, much less express clearly to most others the magnitude of the grief I felt. During this time, I relied heavily on others' ability to express what I could not. Favourite writers, singers and women in my support group were all voices I listened to and identified with until I could speak for myself again. On some occasions I also shared their expressions with family members in an effort to comfort all of us and to convey what I was experiencing.

Poet Audre Lorde was one of the voices I was introduced to by a friend in my support group. Lorde articulates so clearly how critical it is for each of us to find and hold our individual voices in the course of life's challenges (Lorde 1984). Much later, when I had recovered my own voice, this poem appeared - inspired by Audre Lorde's work. What a relief to finally find my *own* voice!

I can rely on the voices of trusted others until I find my own again
- and find it, I will.

Voice

My Voice came back to me one day -
I'd lost It for a time.
My pain had taken It away
Before It reached Its prime.

I didn't know where It could be
Or if It would come back.
There was so much I could not say;
Expression such a lack.

And, then, just like a River
That had to flow through me,
It started with a Trickle
And ended in a Sea.

And now that Sea holds volumes
Of things It has to say;
It surrounds and soothes; immerses me
In the Spirit's way.

Sometimes It mirrors serenity
That speaks of wisdom calm;
Renews, restores, releases me
With Its healing balm.

Sometimes It's full of turbulence,
With lessons It must teach.
It crashes loud against the shore,
That others It may reach.

Sometimes Its quiet ripples
So gently circle out,
To slowly, softly touch the beach
And wash away my doubt.

My Voice came back to me to stay -
Eternal, Moving Sea -
That I may speak the words that were
Designed to flow through me.

For me, the most difficult period of time to cope was the five-week period that passed between the discovery of two masses in my breast and the diagnosis of breast cancer. As difficult as the rest of the experience has been, I have since known in some measure, at least, what I have had to deal with. Once I knew what reality I faced I could begin to grieve, gather my resources and find concrete ways of coping, at least in the short term. Until then, I wandered about in a nebulous wasteland of "what-ifs". Dealing with periods of profound uncertainty such as this one has clearly been my most difficult task in the face of this and other life challenges.

I am learning to live with uncertainty.

Waiting

Knots of fear twist in my gut;
Their tight constrictions sear;
A shadow of foreboding lurks,
Its darkness ever near.

I am told there may be danger,
But no one knows for sure;
And if there is, they still don't know
If there will be a cure.

I have to use a system large
That moves with little speed
In bringing me the answers
That I so quickly need.

I tell my close ones little,
Though I could use their ear;
It seems so cruel to burden them
With unnecessary fear.

So I try to carry on as though
My life is just the same -
Perhaps if I believe it is,
This monster I can tame.

But that just doesn't seem to work;
I don't know how to cope.
In squaring off with the unknown,
How can I dare to hope?

Must I be reaching all the way
Down into my Reserve? -
Or will this be a simple thing
That needs a little nerve?

I don't know what's required of me
'Til I know what I face -
I cannot wait much longer
In this uncertain place!

There were several times throughout the course of discovery, diagnosis, treatment and recovery that I was overwhelmed with fear and pain. Nighttime seemed to be the worst. Yet, that was when I most needed to find some release. Again, use of imagery was a tremendous help in opening myself to Spirit's closeness. Visualizing a nurturing Presence assisted me in letting go of worries and fears, allowing myself to be 'cradled' so I could rest.

That is not to say that I didn't rely on other expressions of Spirit at work. For the first time in my life I took sleeping medication when I desperately needed rest in the hospital. Prior to this, a part of me had believed that for me to do so was to use a 'crutch'. Well, it was - but I could now see that I could no more heal from this trauma without a 'crutch' than I could from a broken leg. (I believe the secret lies in knowing when it is time to throw away the crutch and begin to walk again.) I also relied on herbal tea, aromatherapy, relaxation tapes, back rubs from nurses, reflexology and therapeutic touch to help me release worry and anxiety. The terrifying night I fell asleep with the aid of a First Nations healing tape, a sleeping pill, a therapeutic touch treatment, a back rub, *and* a prayer, I believe I was beginning to trust in and receive *all* of the Creator's gifts as I needed to receive them.

It is okay to rely on all the gifts that can help me to heal,
whatever form they may take.

Cradle Me

Cradle me, Creator Dear -
Please don't let me go.
I'm hurting and I'm terrified -
I need your Presence so.

Cradle me through this long night
As silent tears I weep.
Hold me in your loving arms
And rock me back to sleep.

Cradle me so I may find
Some peace at Your soft breast
I'm tired and I need release -
Creator, help me rest.

Upon diagnosis I was very quickly introduced to one of the harsh realities of dealing with a serious illness - that many critical decisions about treatment need to be made at the very time one is feeling the most overwhelmed and ill-prepared to make them. Confounded by many external barriers to accessing and processing reliable information, I found my sense of bewilderment to be excruciating, particularly because the stakes were so high. I was terrified that I would make the wrong choices - ones which I would later regret either because they had been unsafe or because they were not ones with which I could make my peace. I had no way of knowing with certainty if my choices were the right ones. I *did* know that, ultimately, I was the only one who could or should make them because it was critical to have faith in whatever interventions I chose.

I will make the best decision I can with the resources available to me at the time.

Torn

Rent — Ruptured –

Chasms Deep

Into Body and Soul –

Clefts Exposed

Around me

And within –

Gashes Deepen

As I am Pulled

Between Choices -

All of them as vile

As my vacillation -

As my task of making decisions

Based on evidence as inconclusive as I.

My anguish with regard to treatment choices was most profound in deciding whether or not the loss of my breast was a necessary occurrence, despite the fact that mastectomy was unanimously recommended by the specialists involved. Had there been more than anecdotal evidence available about the effectiveness of non-invasive options, I would most likely have chosen them instead. In the end, I found I had to accept the reality that my illness occurred at a time when there was a woefully inadequate amount of validation available for non-invasive healing measures which were obviously less traumatic and more congruent with my personal belief system. Without this validation I came to realize I was unable to feel safe without the recommended medical interventions, particularly after I became aware that the cancer was more advanced than initially had been thought.

I wrote 'Images' the day before my mastectomy as a way of preparing for, grieving, and reconciling myself to the loss of my breast. Doing so also helped me to start envisioning what meaning could arise from this loss. In addition, this poem helped me to affirm that it is not the form of healing that matters, but its impact. Being alive, feeling at peace and believing in my choices was what mattered.

'Images' is a very intimate poem. As such, I initially hesitated to include it in this collection. In the end, it became clear that it belonged here for two reasons. First, it expresses the significance of a loss that too many women have to experience; I believe it is important to promote a greater collective understanding of that loss if we are to find better alternatives. Second, 'Images' played a very pivotal role in my healing.

It is the one poem I was able to write in the midst of my initial crisis. As you can see, it is very simply written; not one bit of rhyme or rhythm decorate its lines. (I doubt I could have found such embelleshments on that difficult day.) Yet, its writing set the stage for resolution, just as have many pages of unrefined journaling I have written on my healing journey. Again, when it comes to healing, it is not the form that matters, but the impact.

I am learning to live with my losses.

Images...

Of a tentative young lover's hand tenderly caressing you for the first time;
Of impassioned, strong hands holding you close;
Of soft lips and tongue loving you;
Of tiny hands gently milking you as you nourished babes so dear;
Of ready tingles and springs of milk at the sounds of our babies' cries;

Of two lovers learning to join without you;
Of a young woman learning to be whole with only your mate;
Of an old woman, whole, indeed - one-breasted though she be,
Filled with joy to have seen her babies become men
And to have babies and grandbabies of their own,
And to grow old with her beloved,
And to have learned so long ago that her beauty comes from within,
That she is dearly loved by many,
And that, perhaps, God had a higher purpose
For her than she could have realized before;
Her greatest joy is that her babies - who you so lovingly nurtured -
Learned these lessons along with her as they grew -
And they passed them on to their babies,
So that in losing you, the nurturing continued in a way it may not have.

You began it.
Now my arms and my heart will take over
With a greater love and wisdom than they could have known before -
For my sons and for my beloved and for me,
For my grandchildren and great-grandchildren to come -
God give me grace and strength.

Images...

Of a time when such a price won't have to be paid
To heal you and me;
In memory and honour of you
I vow to help that time come.
Please, God, lead the way.

I was blessed with many caring helpers along my healing journey - helpers who chose to 'accompany' me - to go with me on my journey rather than attempting to direct me (Nursing Education Program of Saskatchewan, 1999). Unfortunately, I also encountered some without the ability or inclination to interact with me in such an empowering manner. Rather than being strengthened by such encounters, I was weakened.

In order to avoid becoming totally disempowered, I would put up significant resistance, refusing to be told what to do, especially when I knew there were no clear-cut answers. Not only did these dynamics deplete much-needed energy, they sometimes interfered with receiving the information I so desperately needed in order to make good decisions.

Accompany Me is addressed to those helpers still learning how to accompany those they serve. Having experienced first-hand the impact of an absence of George Gazda's classic "helping skills", I decided to incorporate them into this poem. These skills are warmth, genuineness, respect, concreteness, empathy, self-disclosure and immediacy (Carkhuff 1993; Egan, 1998). Without these skills, helpers can do as much damage as if they lacked the more tangible skills they are expected to possess as professionals. Unfortunately, the harm caused by poor helping skills is not always visible. Therefore, it goes unnoticed, resulting in further trauma. Furthermore, the professionals causing the trauma may not be held accountable.

Accompany Me may be a useful tool for providing feedback and education to those helpers who have complicated rather than facilitated healing. My personal and professional experiences have helped me to develop the conviction that we do ourselves *and* the helper a huge favour when we find the courage to address problems in the therapeutic relationship; that relationship has the potential to be a great source of growth and inspiration for *both* individuals.

I, along with those who assist me, deserve to be
part of a caring, empowering, and strengthening partnership.

Accompany Me

Efficient, skillful, learned one,
On whom I must depend,
Please see the person sitting here,
Not just a wound to mend.

Please focus less on tests and tasks
And more on how I feel;
It really gives a lift to know
That your concern is real.

And 'though it may be that it is,
I sometimes wonder when
You come and go and do your work,
But no warmth and caring lend.

And don't forget it cuts me deep
And undermines my grace
When you advise and condescend
And don't respect my space.

I'd really like to see a glimpse
Of you - the real you -
The one who can relate to pain
And share some insight, too.

I really wish you'd notice all
The things I leave unsaid;
I'd love to talk about them
If I were safely led.

You need to know that helping me
Takes more than concrete skill;
You need to show some competence
In listening to my will.

For I'm the one who's living
With challenges and risk;
I need some understanding,
Not interventions brisk.

I am so very vulnerable;
I need to find my stride
If you will walk along with me,
We both can walk with pride!

I had people ask me if I was angry 'at God' that I was ill. For some reason, I never was. I'm not sure whether this had to do with my pre-existing belief system that *I* was totally responsible for my health - or with the fact that there were so many other legitimate things at which to direct my anger that I never got around to God!

In any event, my anger was one of the most difficult emotions to express. I was fortunate to be comfortable enough to confront professionals on unhelpful or insensitive approaches that infuriated me. However, it took me a long time to find places to express my 'irrational' rage that this whole experience was happening. Wishing not to take it out on my incredibly supportive husband and kids, I tended to push it down inside.

It was finally at my women's cancer support group that I was able to validate my anger enough to begin releasing it. This release was critical, because my anger turned inward was becoming depression. I began to talk more about my anger and to find ways to express my rage when I was alone. For me, journaling was the most powerful avenue of release. From these writings, the creation and sharing of *I'm Angry* emerged as an expression of the tremendous amount of both 'rational' and 'irrational' anger I felt.

I need to acknowledge and express my anger as a necessary part of the healing process.

I'M ANGRY!!!

I'M ANGRY at my body
For behaving in this way.
I'M ANGRY at the people
Who don't know what to say.
I'M ANGRY at professionals
Who don't know how to care.
I'M ANGRY there is danger
Which I must now beware.

I'M ANGRY at the books I read -
They all say different things.
I'M ANGRY at the judgments -
They leave me bitter stings.
I'M ANGRY at toxicity
For putting me at risk.
I'm ANGRY my old life is gone
In one great sudden whisk!

I'M ANGRY at a world in which
Pure living's hard to find.
I'M ANGRY that I cannot do
Just what I had in mind.
I'M ANGRY that my image
Of wholesomeness is gone.
I'M ANGRY that of late I am
So tired, pale and drawn!

I'M ANGRY that the treatments make
Me sick when I felt well.
I'M ANGRY that my story
Is so very hard to tell.
I'M ANGRY I've been traumatized
By scalpels, pokes and prods.
I'M ANGRY they won't give me
The world's most perfect odds!

I'M ANGRY at decisions
That I don't want to make.
I'M ANGRY at the helpers
Whose egos are at stake.
I'M ANGRY at the people
Who would take charge of me.
I'M ANGRY at a system
That sometimes just won't see.

I'M ANGRY at old practices
That take so long to change.
I'M ANGRY at slow research -
Our priorities seem strange.
I'M ANGRY at old paradigms
Long overdue to shift.
I'M ANGRY at the factions
Between which lie a rift.

I'M ANGRY at biomedicine
For not seeing all of me.
I'M ANGRY that alternatives'
Proven worth is yet to be.
I'M ANGRY at the two of them
For not working with the other.
I'M ANGRY it's so hard to choose -
Why do I even bother?!

I'M ANGRY at not knowing
Just what the future holds.
I'M ANGRY I can't make things fit
Into familiar molds.
I'M ANGRY at myself, as well,
For not taking better care.
I'M ANGRY that this life we live
Just isn't at all fair!

I'M ANGRY that the changes
I'd like to make within
Just won't happen overnight.
It seems I just can't win!
I'M ANGRY that the changes
I'd like to make without
Are sometimes not in my control.
It makes me want to SHOUT!

I'M ANGRY that my busy life's
Been stopped right in its tracks.
I'M ANGRY that there's risk involved,
Not guarantees and facts.
I'M ANGRY that this illness
Got such a hold on me.
I'M ANGRY THAT THIS WHOLE THING
EVER HAD TO BE!!!

My work in the mental health field had taught me that support systems are central to well-being, but I had no idea just how critical they are until I was hurting and became the recipient of such support. I have been blessed to belong to a number of strong support systems, all of whom have sustained me in countless thoughtful ways.

The most unique expression of support came from members of the psychiatric nursing community. Not only did they take it upon themselves to attend to the practical matter of feeding my family for about 10 days straight, they decided to throw a 'Bon Voyage Breast' party! This healing gathering took place about a month after my surgery. As the poem describes, it had a powerful impact upon my healing. The opportunity to acknowledge and grieve publicly the transition I was experiencing gave me incredible freedom to be open about my experience. It also taught me much about 'healing with humour', an art that author and breast cancer survivor Cathy Fenwick has addressed so effectively in her book by that name (Fenwick, 1995).

Later on, we decided to share this approach with others through a poster presentation at health-related conferences and through resulting media coverage. We did so, not because we were exhibitionists(!) or because we presumed this kind of gathering to be right for everyone, but because we wished to help people explore how they might be able to mobilize their communities in caring and creative ways to support those amongst them who are hurting. I believe each community that is committed to caring has its own innate wisdom about how to support a particular member - when its members trust in the magic of their collective caring.

It is a sign of strength to embrace the caring
that can be found in community.

Caring Community

My colleagues came together
In close community
To throw me a big party -
Where I never thought *I'd* be!

You see, it was to say good bye
To my departed breast;
I'd recovered from the surgery,
But not from all the rest.

Somehow, they seemed to
know that,
And gathered everyone
Into a healing circle
For some caring and
some fun.

Each one of
them brought
candles
And healing
thoughts to
share.
They brought
some risqué
humour
That no one
else would
dare!

They were
true kindred
spirits
Who skillfully
did bring
Such care and
sensitivity;
They thought of
everything.

They brought me
many symbols
Of healing, life and love,
Convinced I faced a challenge
That I could rise above.

They even brought some tissues -
Enough for everyone! -
But much to everyone's surprise,
The tears just didn't come.

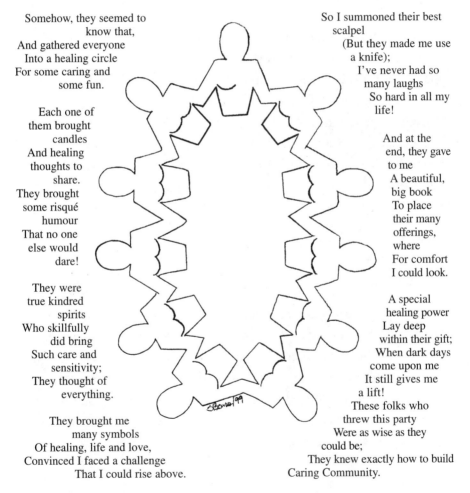

Perhaps it was that sharing
Our time and space that way
Was soothing and uplifting;
Tears weren't needed on that day.

And even though they brought a cake
(A 'boob' - to have some fun),
They still were so respectful;
Who'd cut it? Seems *no one*!

So I summoned their best
scalpel
(But they made me use
a knife);
I've never had so
many laughs
So hard in all my
life!

And at the
end, they gave
to me
A beautiful,
big book
To place
their many
offerings,
where
For comfort
I could look.

A special
healing power
Lay deep
within their gift;
When dark days
come upon me
It still gives me
a lift!
These folks who
threw this party
Were as wise as they
could be;
They knew exactly how to build
Caring Community.

I wish that all folks hurting
Had such Community
To strengthen and sustain them -
What healing we would see!

Having read many books about the power of the mind-body connection in healing, I was determined to maintain a positive attitude about my situation. I remember saying, "If I can keep my spirits up, I'll be okay". Consequently, I pushed away a lot of legitimate grief, confusing it with the onset of a 'negative attitude'.

This approach lasted until about half-way through my chemo when I entered a low time that was to last many months. Perhaps my defenses were low enough that I finally had to give in to the overwhelming sadness I felt in response to the many losses my illness had elicited. I found myself grieving the many temporary losses such as my work, my hair, my energy level, and my general sense of well-being. I also grieved the loss of my former self-image which had generally been one of health and 'wholesomeness'. Most of all, I grieved the loss of the illusion that life has guarantees of safety. All I could do to find comfort was to try to maintain my belief that forces bigger than I would guide me through this emotional desert.

I was very grateful for the perspective offered to me in a book a friend gave me during that desolate time, *Life-Threatening Illness and the Search for Meaning* by Jean Shinoda Bolen. In her book, Dr. Bolen honours the power of the mind-body connection, yet also honours the place of grief in the process of healing. She describes it as a 'descent into the underworld' which is necessary for healing and eventual transformation to take place (Bolen, 1996). The validation offered to me by her balanced approach and others' like it was a wonderful gift of permission to honour *all* of my emotions, whether they be painful or uplifting.

Giving in to my sadness frees me to grieve fully, openly, and healthily.

Heartsick

Heartsick with sadness
Beyond belief;
Gut-wrenching grief
I still can't shake;
It will not break.

Heartsick with sadness
Life's so hard.
My hopes retard.
I've no joy.
Tears I employ.

Heartsick with sadness;
I ache inside.
I want to hide.
I feel so blue.
Will I renew?

Heartsick with sadness;
It's hard to pray.
Can't see my way.
Spirit, come near
Spirit, be here.

In the midst of my low time, I was torn between the need to remain in the safe cocoon of our own home and the need to get away from the isolation and routine demands that were becoming overwhelming to me toward the end of chemotherapy. I had little reserve left to offer my family and I was consumed with guilt over not being emotionally 'there' for them after all the support they had constantly provided me. It became clear after an exhausting weekend that I needed to retreat.

I knew exactly where I needed to go - *home* to my parents. It had been a long time since I had felt this vulnerable, this much in need of their nurturing. Fortunately, for me, they had certainly not forgotten how to offer it freely, lovingly, and wisely.

I think it helped all of us to spend that time together. Letting my parents help me in a way that I would not have before, allowed me to receive exactly what I needed. Allowing myself to be vulnerable created an opportunity for them to give me a gift that no one else could possibly have given.

Allowing myself to be vulnerable in safe places helps me to receive the nurturing I need.

Haven

Overwhelmed with mundane tasks,
Sick and tired of wearing masks,
Being brave, doing what they ask,
I need to free my soul to bask.

Although their love is my lifeline,
For time and space I surely pine;
Still, I need close ones of mine,
The warmth of a familiar shrine.

So, to a haven I know well
I retreat for just a spell
To ones who came each time I fell
Who listened when I had to tell

The woes of life, the tragic tale;
The times I was convinced I'd fail,
They'd hold me close and let me wail,
And, then, persuade me I could sail.

Such a boost is what I need -
This howling hunger they can feed;
This tired traveler they can lead;
Their love will let my healing speed.

Two so dear, so wise and kind -
My weakness they don't seem to mind;
They walk the road, 'though it may wind,
Helping me the way to find.

They open their beloved abode,
That I may lighten up my load;
They freely share their caring mode
All along life's rugged road.

And when I'm whole and well again
The lessons taught will still remain:
Of how to love someone in pain,
Of how to soothe when spirits wane.

I treasure these two teachers dear
Who nurtured me through pain and fear,
Who cried and dried my every tear;
Their kind of love I strive to mirror.

A haven, too, I will create
For those I love who find a state
Wherein they must just watch and wait
Or sort out questions of their fate.

And may it fill with tender care -
The kind I've seen these teachers share,
The kind you know is always there -
A precious gift of Spirit rare.

Around the time I gave in to the fact that I was going to be sad for as long as I needed to be, I began to re-examine the expectations and images in my head. It became very clear to me I was still trying to control everything about the healing process (including how long it should take!) It was as if I were trying to drive a car down a road I somehow pictured as being straight with an end in full sight. A more realistic picture was that I was on a river with a life all its own and *no* end in sight. While I had *some* control, I had to give in to the elements around me, too. I decided I had better stop 'driving' and learn to 'sail'. I began journaling around this imagery each morning, especially when I could feel my anxiety and need for control escalate. As I described in the introduction, *Sailing Out* eventually emerged.

It takes as long as it takes.

Sailing Out

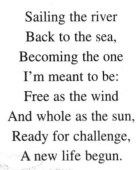

Sailing the river
Back to the sea,
Becoming the one
I'm meant to be:
Free as the wind
And whole as the sun,
Ready for challenge,
A new life begun.

But the river is long.
The journey is slow.
Healing the hurt
And letting it go
Takes time and good sailing,
Trust in the Breeze,
Mastering currents,
Yet gliding with ease.

Sailing past fear
And dregs of regret,
Past yesterday's choices,
Patterns I've set.
Sailing with courage,
New strength and resolve;
I face only forward
So I can evolve.

Soon will the seaside
Appear up ahead
So my journey will broaden
And my Power will spread.
Like spirals in seashells
My healing will rise
And I will sail out -
Mellow, gentle and wise.

As my anxiety and sadness began to dissipate, I found myself experiencing an emotional void that I still don't entirely understand. While it was anesthetizing to feel less emotional pain, it was troubling to feel *nothing*; I had anticipated feeling relieved and invigorated at being able to resume my life. Instead, I was frozen.

Perhaps I was simply worn out - physically, emotionally, mentally, and spiritually. Perhaps I was bored by having been on the sidelines for so long. It almost felt like I was insulated from everything and everybody. Perhaps my Creator knew I needed space and rest before I could move on. In any case, it eventually did pass, becoming one more experience that has taught me the course of healing is unpredictable.

I will trust in the Wisdom of my Guide.

Numb

Nebulous nothingness; stymied, numb
Where's this vacant vacuum from?
Have no voice; just stay mum;
Tongue is still, expression dumb.

Only know one note to hum;
Only have one chord to strum;
Only hear one beat to drum.
Will my music ever come?

And, too, with close ones,cannot feel;
Simply have no zest nor zeal.
Do I need this void to heal?
Before the Spirit I will kneel.

As I prepared to return to work many weeks after chemotherapy ended, my cocoon of numbness was cracked wide open. I began to feel incredibly vulnerable, my dulled emotions now having shifted to ones of great intensity. I knew that leaving the isolation of my home and returning to work that I loved was part of my healing. Still, I felt so vulnerable after the year's events that I wondered if I was still too emotionally fragile to deal with the demands I knew I would face in my workplace. In addition, I simply did not have my usual physical stamina.

I was blessed to have a very caring vocational counselor who had the wisdom and creativity to assist me in planning a very gradual return-to-work plan. It was like receiving a wonderful gift - the gift of time. I was able to take a considerable period in which to work up to full-time hours. Doing so was worth every penny of the employment income I lost by staying on my disability plan.

It was during this time that I began to write, finally able to articulate and to begin working through the profound trauma of the previous months. Yet I also was able to reconnect with the familiar roles and responsibilities I had missed so much, gradually re-building my physical and emotional endurance.

Many are not so lucky. Inflexible systems and attitudes in the medical and insurance systems often force people back to work at an unrealistic and destructive pace. I believe more emphasis on allowing time for 'curing' *and* healing is needed, particularly given the growing body of evidence linking unresolved grief and stress to many types of illness (Pert, 1997; Quinn, 1996).

I need time, space and purpose to heal.

Raw

Exposed and raw and traumatized,
I face the world at last;
Although it seems the 'curing's' done,
The healing's not so fast.

Something tells me that it's time
To now pick up the pace,
But my soul just feels too overwhelmed
To run the usual race.

And, yet, my soul is asking me
For challenge and routine;
From the comforts of my safe cocoon
I now must slowly wean.

But as I carefully venture out,
Can I protect myself?
Resilience and tolerance
Lie somewhere on a shelf;

And so my faith and confidence
Are waning day by day;
I've been invaded oft enough -
I can't afford to stray;

If further hurt should ambush me
When I'm out there alone,
It may defeat and violate
And cut me to the bone.

Will arrows of anxiety
And trouble come my way?
Because I know life must go on,
I'm pretty sure they may.

Those arrows may just open up
Old wounds that still aren't healed;
Then I would be so much at risk,
My progress all repealed.

I can't go out there on my own -
Creator, 'round me keep;
Shield me with Your armor light,
So they won't pierce too deep;

Guide me - and those arrows, too -
That I may have some time
To tend my wounds just as they need,
Amidst Your love sublime.

My former belief that I was totally in charge of my life and my health set me up for much angst when I found myself facing a life-threatening illness. Months of self-blame ensued despite the fact that, rationally, I knew there were likely many factors - many which I may never identify.

All it takes is a look around to notice dramatic inconsistencies in who gets sick and who doesn't - who experiences painful life experiences and who doesn't - to know that it's not that simple; a healthy approach to life does not guarantee us immunity to illness or hard times. Besides, all of us have unhealthy habits and environments of some kind. If healthy, positive outcomes were so directly related to our actions, wouldn't we all be sick or traumatized - all the time?!

Again, a friend from support group shared with me a powerful article written by Val Paape called *Guilt as a Chronic Illness*. In the article Paape challenges the simplistic contemporary mentality that "our future and well-being are up to us, that our choices determine everything from our health to our financial status" (Paape, 1996, p.40). My friend's timing was impeccable; I was finally ready to listen to Paape's message which was very similar to the one my husband and other close ones had been trying to send me for months. Reading the article opened the flood gates inside me, allowing me to finish writing *Questions*. Interestingly, after I experienced the resolution that came with writing this poem, I could not stop writing and processing other earlier reactions and experiences. Acceptance was a powerful release.

I still believe my approach to life is a key factor in my health and happiness. I also know I need to take responsibility for making changes I believe will help me heal. However, I am learning I do not control everything that happens to me. Accepting that reality is helping me to respond more constructively and creatively, allowing my illness to teach me rather than to destroy me.

Ultimately, I will accept what is.

Questions

Questions keep on coming 'round.
They never seem to quit
Trying to make sense of things.
Yet, answers just won't fit.
I just don't understand how
Bad things could come my way
And why this huge catastrophe
Has come with me to stay!

Did I betray my body
Or did it betray me?
If I'm in charge of living,
Then how'd this come to be?
If life is what you make it
Did I, somehow, allow
This illness to take charge of me?
And if I did, what now?

If wellness is a state of mind,
Then where's my mind been at?
If illness is increasing,
Does that make me a stat?
Could I have prevented it?
If I had only known!
I would have lived life perfectly
If I thought I was this prone!

How do I be responsible
Without feeling it's my fault?
How do I choose safe living
And not come to a halt?
How do I find harmony
In this discordant space?
And how do I find balance in
A world that goes this pace?

Do I control the outcome
If I do all the 'right things'?
What if I just try too hard
And clip my healing's wings?
How do I stay positive
When I'm so sad I'm sick?
And if I grieve for too long now
Does that mean that I'm licked?

How do I resume my life
When nothing is the same?
And what should I be changing
When a 'cause' I still can't name?
Not knowing what holds danger
Do I know when to swerve?
How can I trust in life again
When it's thrown me this curve?

When will I ignore again
The usual aches and pains?
How do I 'get on with it'
While my whole spirit wanes?
How do I tell denial from
A new-found strength and calm?
And if I feel too confident,
Is that a risky balm?

Why won't all the answers come?
Right now I need them bad!
Will resolution ever be?
I feel like I've been had!
When will I sort out all this
Confusing paradox?
Why can't health be fit into
A nice, neat, little box?

Perhaps because pat answers
Won't heal me, anyway.
In trust and full acceptance my
Serenity will lay;
Seems Time's the Gentle Healer
That brings peace within reach
So that truths begin to surface
And questions, then, can teach.

For now, I must be patient,
'Though I don't like to wait.
I like to have things finished
And in a perfect state.
Perhaps I'll never know why
This fate has come to me,
But I think it's going to teach me
To just let some things be!

It seems all of us have a need to speculate about the reasons for bad things happening in our own and others' lives. I certainly recognized this strong tendency within myself as I struggled to make sense of my own baffling experience. I also recognized it within myself in the way that I had formerly made private, if not openly-stated, assumptions - even judgments - about why a certain fate might have befallen someone. I also recognized it in generally well-intentioned comments or questions some would share with friends, family or myself about why this crisis might have happened for me. (*I* was totally bewildered by it; how could *they* presume to speculate?) I recognize this need most blatantly in the pop self-help literature that often reinforces the notion that somehow "we can choose our life off a shelf", as one of my brothers puts it. While there is much literature that does a wonderful job of enhancing our awareness of how our spirituality, our living and our health are inter-connected, there is much which oversimplifies and which promotes a sense of guilt amongst those of us who have already undergone upheaval in any one of these areas. Is our collective need for an illusion of control so strong sometimes that we must grope for black and white answers at the expense of those most in need of compassion and simple acceptance - acceptance that, sometimes, living and being human is just plain difficult?

I was comforted and amused by a story my Mom shared with me as I wrestled with my own and others' perceptions of my dilemma. The story was about a dear aunt of mine who had been undergoing a series of ordeals during a particular period of her life. A well-meaning acquaintance had shared with her the well-known axiom: "Well, God never gives us more than He knows we can handle". With her characteristic wit and spunk, my aunt replied, "Well, I wish He didn't have such confidence in me, then!!!" She tells me humbly that it is not an original retort. In any case, her use of it was well-timed and instructional!

I hope I am able to cope with future onslaughts of truism with such perspective. Even more so, I hope I can refrain from conjecture about others' circumstances and experiences. Instead, I hope to be able to simply help support them so *they* can find the grace and strength to cope with and, perhaps, eventually to find some meaning in devastating circumstances and experiences.

Only my Creator and I can interpret the meaning of my painful experiences.

Postulations. . .

"It MUST be stress, it seems to me,
That brought this on - it HAS to be!"

"Most likely 'cause she worked so hard
And had no time for home nor yard!"

"But, then, I know that other dame -
She stayed at home - her fate's the same!"

"Well, I don't know, but I am sure
She didn't eat nor live so pure!"

"Too little rest and exercise
And too much sun, I will surmise."

"Mind you, we haven't had a walk
In 'way too long, how can we talk?"

"But, then, we live right, I suppose;
We seem to steer past all those woes."

"Perhaps it is the Dear Lord's will
That some must take a bitter pill."

"I guess that's just how some folks learn;
They need a trial at every turn."

"'Though I'm not one to criticize,
'Tis true, I do hypothesize."

"We've got it cased, I do presume -
Not that WE would just ASSUME!"

Easter-time the year after my cancer diagnosis was the Easter of Easters. My perspective had begun to return, my spirits had begun to lift and my own hair was long enough to reveal! I was beginning to feel joy despite my realization that life holds no guarantees. Instead of feeling constantly terrorized by this lack of control, I began to feel freed by it. As a result, I strongly identified with the seasonal themes of suffering, resurrection, and new life.

My journaling throughout Lent revealed a recurring cycle of responses that I likened to repeated small 'Easter Experiences'. I also likened them to the healing spirals spoken of in First Nations traditional stories, wherein we experience the same lessons over and over again, learning them at a little deeper level each time. Hence, *Spirit Spiral* emerged on Easter Monday.

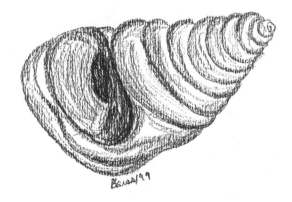

I learn the lesson better each time it is presented.

Spirit Spiral

Terror, Courage,
Peace, then Joy:
A spiral Spirit-led.
Terror, Courage,
Peace, then Joy:
Full life and trust ahead ...

With each round
The learnings grow,
The lettings-go increase.
In losing charge,
Illusion fades,
True Power finds release.

For Terror met
With Courage strong
Gives rise to soul-deep Peace.
That victory won,
New Joy resides
And trivial trappings cease.

Yet, Terror comes
Again to bear;
I can't deny her power -
But Courage meets
Her at the edge
To serve her finest hour.

Each time she goes
She's faster still
And firmer in her stand.
She won't allow
Terror inside.
She leaves all in God's hand.

So comes the Peace
Again to stay,
A little longer now.
Re-enters Joy
To celebrate
The wonder of God's vow -

A vow to soar
At spiral's end
As trust becomes complete,
Free from care
And false control,
Oh, full existence sweet!

I remember saying to friends in the early weeks of my illness, "If I can laugh as much as I cry, I'll be okay." I wasn't always able to maintain this balance. In fact, in the later low time I rarely laughed at all even though friends kept me well-supplied with humourous reading material. This lack of joy worried me because I know that laughter is extremely healing - physically, mentally, emotionally, and spiritually (Fenwick, 1995). Still, it was easier said than done when my spirits were low.

The support group I began attending toward the end of chemotherapy was a tremendous catalyst in re-kindling my sense of humour because we could share jokes that spoke to our pain in a way that we may not have been able to anywhere else. At the risk of seeming inappropriate, I have decided to share with others some of that bizarre, but extremely healing humour I recovered in the group. I believe it is good for us to laugh at that which terrifies us most - when the time is right.

One final comment: There was a day when I would have had to ensure the columns of this poem would be even. This time, I purposely left it alone to symbolize my learning to live with asymmetry. (It's a good thing!)

I can find release amidst devastation.

Laughter CANcer Vive!!!

Laughter *CAN*cer Vive
This twisted tragedy.
It bubbles up between the tears,
So healing and so free.

It helps me reconcile
The irony I face.
It lifts my spirits, puts my mind
Into a better space.

It helps me catch the fun
In all my moments now
So even if they, too, bring pain,
A chuckle they endow.

For example, diagnosis
Came on convocation day;
My 'Bachelor: Health Science'
Sure brought no health my way!

And there's the moment I observed
My breast was no big loss -
A literal statement, to be sure
(My "Cup 'A'" wasn't boss)!

It's really quite hilarious
Anatomy so small
Could bring me such gigantic grief -
And back me to the wall!

Then, there's the day I asked my doc
When my fake boob was due.
He looked me up and down and said,
"Four weeks, not six - for you."

So, I assumed my healing
Was superior to most,
But it was because I was without
Much weight up front to boast!

I remember shopping for
My first new bra in years.
It's crazy that just wearing one
Was one of my worst fears!

It really seemed quite silly
To don one so I could
Accommodate one single breast,
When, with two, I seldom would.

And don't you think it's funny,
Now there's only one to pet,
I've had more men come feel me up
Than when I had the set?!

And what a gas someone like me -
Once one for rigid symmetry
In act, in dress, in life, in all -
Is now lop-sided as can be!

And isn't it a real snort
How I now bare my soul -
When I used to be a private sort?
- At breasts I now cajole!

Then, there's the time my hair and I
Had such a falling out.
Those were the worst of "bad hair days"
To ever come about!

And in good time, it all grew back.
'Twas then I really knew
That chemo truly was enough
To make one's hair curl, too!

You know, it really sets me off
When people say with stun,
"You're much too young for cancer!"
Well, isn't everyone?!

I have to stuff a huge guffaw
When someone says to me,
"It's awful to be getting old!"
It's what I'd like to be!

Oh, yes, it's truly been a hoot
All along the way;
And, yes, this quirky side of me
Has full intent to stay!

Laughter *CAN*cer Vive!
It's critical to give
Because, translated, it becomes
'Laughter/Cancer - LIVE!!!'

It had taken me a considerable length of time to feel comfortable wearing a wig. As nice at it was, I still felt like 'I had a cat on my head', as one of my friends in the support group put it. Also, I hated the very word; from day one, I referred to it as 'my other hair'.

In addition to numerous other adjustments, I grieved the loss of my hair even more than I grieved the loss of my breast. This reaction puzzled me initially, but I think it had to do with the fact that my hair was a much more visible part of my body. My breast had never been a big part of my body image (let's face it - it had never been a big part of my body!) However, my hair had always been a favourite part of my appearance. To top it all off (pardon the pun), its absence proclaimed publicly that I was a 'cancer patient'. To lose it, even temporarily, was devastating.

I came to deeply appreciate 'my other hair' for looking so real that many thought it was my own. Of course, I felt tremendous relief and joy when my own returned - with curls to boot!

I will adapt to the changes at hand.

My Other Hair

Now, I will share about "My Other Hair"
(I would not wear a "wig" -
I hate that small word; it sounds so absurd -
Like I'm some phony prig!).

My hair all fell out; that's what came about
(Just a temporary glitch);
So, I had no choice; that sure gave a voice
To that nice clerk's great sales pitch!

I was in a pinch; it was a real cinch
I needed cover up top.
'Though it was no deal, it sure made me feel
Like I had a wondrous mop!

And it looked so real; it had such appeal
That most would simply chat,
"You have a new style!" I'd have to smile
And say, "Something like that!!"

So I wore it a lot (not when it was hot
'Cause I'd break out in a sweat).
We got along fine, 'though I sure did pine
For my own soft locks to pet.

Then came a big hitch - things began to itch
As my own hair came back in.
I soon did get like a 'chia pet',
Then, the real growth did begin.

So, rig-a-jig-jig, soon I flipped my wig
(Then I didn't mind that term!);
A moment big - a real 'shin-dig' -
'Cause beneath – I found a PERM!!

Now, that's quite a zap! Chemo gets a bad rap
But maybe I can't complain;
'Though it made me hurl, it gave my hair curl,
So I'll temper my disdain!

But, "My Other Hair", you were, oh, so fair -
There never was a doubt!
You were always there while my head was bare -
Your merits I still tout!

So, wherever you are (you will go far -
'Cause I gave you up for loan) -
You'll stand some head in real good stead
While it is baldish-prone!

My husband and I had planned to have a big party when 'this was all over'. As time went on, we began to realize that there was not going to be a day when someone would tell us, "Congratulations! You're cured! You did it!" Even if someone could have brought us such jubilant tidings - Is our journey of healing and learning and growing ever finished, anyway?

As more time passed, we discovered that there were certainly celebrations to be held along the way, nevertheless. Because of the intensity of my reaction to 'my other hair', I decided to make a celebration out of its departure from my life. One friend jokingly suggested a wig-burning party! While it was initially tempting, I decided I wanted to mark the occasion a little more constructively. Not only had I become somewhat attached to the familiar rug; I wanted someone else to be able to have some nice 'other hair', too. So, I decided to donate it to a volunteer group that distributes them through the local cancer centre. I packaged it up in a pretty bag in which Canadian Cancer Society 'Reach to Recovery' volunteers had brought some items after my surgery. Doing so helped me symbolically close the door on the active medical treatment era of my journey.

A dear friend accompanied me on this little mission that took place on a sunny spring day. Afterwards, we walked the trails near the cancer centre and I shared with her the beginnings of this book. It was a wonderful way to say good-bye and to celebrate the healing that was occurring. However, the memory that is most vivid from that morning is the bouquet of pussy willows that my friend brought me as a symbol of renewal. I think *Pussy Willow* captures best the meaning that gesture had for me.

I can celebrate happy moments along the way, even as the journey must continue.

Pussy Willow

Pussy Willow, soft and new,
You celebrate with me
This sparkling special day of spring!
Our new growth is set free!

Tiny pearls of wisdom bud;
New growth is everywhere -
Just like fresh locks upon my head
That curl so softly there …

And soon a transformation
Will surely come about;
With Sun and Rain and Time, our whole
Inside will all leaf out!

And, too, your fine stems show me
The growth I feel within;
We're supple, yet we're strong and tough -
And ready to begin!

Pussy Willow, soft and new,
You celebrate with me
This day - this special spring of springs!
Our new growth is set free!

I had initially considered ridding myself of all the items that reminded me
of cancer and the unpleasant active medical treatment I had undergone. It
seemed that doing so would symbolize my readiness to move on, leaving
behind the emotional and physical pain associated with that period of time.
However, the scarves my mother had made me were not something with
which I could part. I am so grateful to have trusted my intuition on this one.
I believe it was telling me that I cannot (nor do I want to) completely
abandon my painful experiences; they are as much a part of me as are the
joyful ones.

My joys and my hurts continually shape who I am becoming.

Scarves

My mother sewed some pretty scarves
To wear on my bare head.
"I put some love in every stitch,"
To me she softly said.

When I wrapped those pretty scarves
Around my barren crown
I felt so swaddled in her love;
They eased my furrowed frown.

Now, I wear those pretty scarves
Around my open throat;
They look so chique and suave, and yet,
With Mother-Love they dote.

Those scarves remind me of the love
That saw me through my trials,
And of transitions that took place
From tears of grief to smiles.

All those are now a part of me;
With me they still belong;
Just like my scarves, they are transformed
And simply come along;

Adorning my evolving self
With dancing patterns bright,
They wrap me in their drapes and folds
And feel so real and right.

I will wear those pretty scarves
Through all my joys and strife;
They'll mix and match with all that comes
To decorate my life!

I have a new question to ask any young person who seeks my counsel on choosing a life partner: "Can you envision the person loving you and tending to your needs when you are bald, sick and missing a body part?" (While it is hardly a fair question to include in the want-ads of the personal section, I think it's a good one!) I would also say to such an inquisitor, "If you think the answer is 'yes' and you can envision being able to provide the same for your intended, I would be willing to venture a guess that you have the Right One."

In all honesty, it's not a question I ever really thought about - nor ever thought I would have to. Fortunately, I had the Right One. While we both continue to experience many changes and challenges to sort out, we are blessed to be emerging in closer partnership than ever. *Partner Mine* says the rest.

I am intended to be loved unconditionally.

Partner Mine

Partner Mine, you've seen me through
My very darkest days.
You give me strength to lean upon
With your accepting ways.

You loved me when I loathed myself,
When ugly, tired, and beat
I could not see the good in me;
You kept me from defeat.

You loved me with your actions,
Not empty words and talk.
You never wavered as you took
The road we had to walk.

If, at times, things overwhelm
You never let it show;
But if you do - that's okay, too -
I really hope you know.

Your steadiness amazes me,
Your gentleness and calm
For when you hold me close and firm
It's like I'm in God's palm.

Partner Mine, you've shared my life
Through all its joys and tears.
You are the one God meant for me
Throughout the passing years.

One of the things I worried most about during my illness was how to express my feelings openly and honestly without frightening or further traumatizing our two sons. I wanted them to feel secure and strong. Yet, often, I didn't feel that way myself. How, then, could I model and foster these qualities?

As kids do, they asked questions spontaneously in addition to the intentional talks my husband or I initiated. We had some 'heart-to-hearts' that went a long way towards healing as a family. Through these discussions, I gradually learned that they knew me too well for me to be able to hide my feelings. I gradually learned that I might as well stop trying to cover them up. In fact, it became clear that they worried even more when they could see I was trying to hide something. My kids were teaching me. Their wisdom helped me learn to let go of unrealistic fronts and expectations of myself. *Careful Traveler*, the translation of my oldest son's name, is a tribute to that son who was 11 at the time of diagnosis.

It is healing for all of us when I share my hurts with loved ones.

Careful Traveler

Careful Traveler, my first born -
You're steady and you're strong.
You're open and you've understood,
Shown balance all along
This rocky path we've had to walk,
Though it's been hard and long.

You've tackled fears with confidence,
Yet let us know if there
Were things you had to talk about
And treated all with care;
And 'though I wish pain hadn't come,
You've learned some lessons rare.

You've learned life's not a given
To be taken as we please;
We're all here for a purpose,
Amidst uncertainties.
You're learning young to deal with that -
With faith you'll learn to see.

You'll see that Spirit's near you
In everything you do.
You'll see that if things do go wrong,
It's always there for you.
You'll feel Its presence 'round you
To strengthen and renew.

Careful Traveler, you must know
Your presence on this trail
Has helped to heal my wounds and hurts
Through loving without fail.
I am so blessed to be your Mom -
Your love and life I hale!

Many weeks after my chemotherapy was over, our youngest son, who was eight at the time of diagnosis, began experiencing some difficulties in relationships at school. The usual measures were not successful in circumventing the troublesome behavior in which he was engaging. One night, when the situation 'came to a head', he admitted in response to direct questioning that he was still afraid I was going to die. Tears and questions began to flow, revealing that he had been consumed with this fear even though he had said nothing. Instead, he had acted out his insecurity at school.

When I later asked him what had kept him from sharing his fears earlier, he replied "I didn't want to make you sad". He was visibly relieved when I replied that nothing could make me more sad than knowing he was hurting inside and not sharing it with anyone. We had a good long cry together that eventually transformed into laughter. The relief we both felt was palpable; we did not have to - nor *could* we - protect one another with silence.

Afterwards, I reminded him that it was okay to share his worries with anyone else he chose. His hurried reply of 'Ya, Ya, Mom, I know!', as he went off to play, suggested to me that he was beginning to feel more secure again. The ensuing turn-around in his behavior at school was another affirmation that he was on his way to healing.

Long after this time, he very matter-of-factly told me that the fear of losing me would always be there for him. Fortunately, the return of his characteristic enthusiasm for life and living reassures us that he, too, is learning to trust in the face of life's uncertainties.

No matter what life brings, my loved ones and I will be okay
if we trust one another and the Process.

God's Precious Gift

You finally came to ask of me
The questions in your heart.
My dear, young son, the truth you seek;
Where will I ever start?

You tell me you're still scared I'll die;
You want to know the truth.
What words are wise and clear and fair
So early in your youth?

Although the future looks so bright,
I can't say what I would -
I cannot give you absolutes -
But, then, I never could.

We've never known how long we have
In our existence here,
But I believe Eternal Life
Can calm our lingering fear.

It breaks my heart to find out that
I cannot just appease.
Did you really have to learn so young
Life has few certainties?

But, you've learned whatever life may bring,
You're going to be okay
Because Spirit is a part of you,
Especially when you pray.

You've also learned it's good to cry
When you hurt inside.
Old rules and lies can fall away -
By those you shan't abide.

You've also brought me healing, son;
This sharing is a lift.
You truly are what your name says -
You are "God's precious gift".

My parents-in-law, who live in the same community as we do, have supported us in countless ways on a day-to-day basis throughout the course of my illness and recovery. They not only contributed significantly to our healing, but they taught us much about how to help someone through a tough time with respect, practicality and inspiration. For these reasons, I have included, with their permission, this tribute I wrote for them.

The acts of love I experience teach me and heal me.

A Special Place

Co-creators of my beloved,
You are a blessing rare.
You have seen us through
some troubling times
With wisdom and with care.

You treated me with such respect;
You trusted I would find
The path that would be right for me,
Then came and walked behind.

You have stayed behind us all the way
Through all our ups and downs,
Yet knew when we must walk alone
Within our private bounds.

You never minded times I came
And had to shed a tear;
You never shied away from pain,
Willing to share our fear.

You found so many helpful things
To share from day to day;
Your hugs, your meals, your music soft
Helped keep our angst at bay.

Perhaps the greatest gift you gave
Was faith and hope 'midst strife -
The kind you've modeled for us all
Throughout our family life.

But, no, the greatest gift for me
Is one from long ago -
A loving partner in my life
Whom you have nurtured so.

You've loved and celebrated all
The gifts he has to give;
You showed him gentle strength
and grace;
You taught him how to live.

And, too, you've taught the two of us
With your example strong
The secrets of a lasting love
To share our whole lives long.

I cannot ever tell you what
Your love has meant to me;
Inside my heart's a special place
For which you hold the key.

This poem is a tribute to three of my closest friends. Each supported me in her own unique way at the times I needed her most.

One friend accompanied me on the shopping trip of a lifetime - the one on which I set out to purchase my breast prosthesis and began the quest for 'my other hair'. It takes a special friend to gracefully support someone pondering the virtues of one 'rug' over another. It takes more than that to hang in there as she contends with her friend's humiliation over coming home empty-handed (or empty-bra-ed?!) because the store has to special order a prosthesis *small* enough!! Amidst tears and laughter, we actually ended up having fun on this bizarre little spree!

Another friend bravely and reverently shaved off the last wisps of my hair when I no longer was willing to contend with the shedding process that chemotherapy had instigated. After a good cry, a good laugh, and some 'girl talk' about what becoming hats and turbans I could now sport, we were off for one of the most enjoyable evening outings I can remember.

The other friend for whom I wrote this poem is the one who dropped everything (including full-time work, two kids, and a husband) for a few days to come from out of town and stay with me during a despairing time. My guilt over this sacrifice evaporated when she told me she had been waiting for the time when I would need her. It was so good to see her that my spirits were initially lifted. As the visit went on, however, she experienced, listened to, and accepted me at my worst. Then, she drove me to the 'haven' of my parents' home.

As the healing process has continued, it has become very important to find a way to tell these friends how critical their presence has been during that process. I cannot imagine how I would have navigated each of the above hurdles without that particular friend - each of whom was exactly the right person for the time. Each one of them is a critical part of my story.

Friends are precious and unique expressions of the Creator's Presence.

Friend

Precious, patient, caring Friend,
We've been through thick and thin;
You've helped my many wounds to heal;
My strength you underpin.

You helped me with unsavory tasks
We didn't want to face;
You took them on courageously,
With wisdom and with grace.

You helped me when I had to cry;
You stood in there with me,
Prepared to meet my demons so
One day they'd set me free.

You always helped me find some laughs
'Midst loss, despair and pain,
Convinced the good times in my life
Would soon return again.

In those good times we both share
The joys of life and love;
We share good fun and company
And gifts from up Above.

Precious, patient, caring friend,
We've been through thick and thin;
Throughout the course of our whole lives,
We'll always be akin.

Every tragedy comes with a gift in hand. This was the title of a presentation by First Nations story-teller and family therapist Dr. Terry Tafoya which I had the privilege of attending the spring one year after my diagnosis (Canadian Association of Psychosocial Oncology, 1997).

Every tragedy comes with a gift in hand. Hmmm. There are many tragedies I would have much difficulty seeing in this light - at least in this lifetime. However, this statement rings clear and true in relation to my own set of challenges to date.

For me, one of the greatest gifts my experience has brought has been the awareness of how important it is to share with others what needs to be said - *when it needs to be said.* I am so grateful to have been given ways to express, individually, in a variety of ways what those important to me have meant in my life. I am also grateful that my husband and I belong to families where such expressions have been met with acceptance.

I would like to share a reflection on a collective tribute to all in our family network of support, a quilt block created for the 'Life Quilt for Breast Cancer' begun by Vancouver breast cancer survivor, Judy Reimer. Judy's work, along with that of many others, has enabled many Canadians to create and share such 'visual meditations' on the experience of breast cancer. In doing so, our individual networks have been honoured and strengthened.

Our family's quilt block contribution included a symbol chosen by or in honour of each immediate and extended family member, reflecting an aspect of living or healing important to that individual. I am so grateful to be nurtured and sustained by this 'Healing Web' which interconnects with the world around us and reminds me of the gifts I have been offered.

Healing happens within relationship.

Healing Web

The inter-locking fabric
Of life, of loss, of love
Is fastened firm by common threads
That serve to rise above
The fear, despair and sadness
Of the challenges we face;
In this sacred web of healing
Our blessings interlace.

My piece connects with others
Who have walked a similar way,
Supported by our loved ones
Whose gifts all interplay
To weave close webs of healing
Round each - round you, round me -
And join the wider healing web
In full community.

Within each special corner
Are symbols of each one
Whose love sustains and strengthens
Through creative caring spun
Against a backdrop hailing
The ordinary day
And days of celebration;
Their patterns interlay.

It honours past and present
And femininity,
Along with all that nurtures
And brings what's meant to be.
Surrounded by the symbols
Of many others' lives,
My own is given greater power
And new-found strength arrives.

The inter-locking fabric
Of life, of loss, of love
Is fastened firm by common threads
That serve to rise above
The fear, despair, and sadness
Of the challenges we face;
In this sacred web of healing
Our blessings interlace.

It has been a joyful and essential task to find words that convey in some measure the immense gratitude I feel toward all those who have supported me throughout the ups and downs of my healing. Among those people are the many professional healers whom I have encountered along the way. I have come to associate the term 'healer' with individuals from a wide variety of disciplines who:

- contribute to my healing by applying their expertise with caring competence
- demonstrate a commitment to acknowledging *all* aspects of my health including the mental, emotional, spiritual, and physical
- acknowledge the impact of phenomenological and individual factors upon health and healing, adopting neither a simplistic 'blame the victim' approach nor a rigidly 'scientific' one
- facilitate truly informed consent by being knowledgeable, open, honest, and empowering in sharing information about what assistance they have to offer
- believe in my ability to heal while acknowledging the reality that life holds no guarantees
- treat each encounter as an opportunity to be a healing presence
- are individuals clearly committed to their own growth and healing
- I intuitively respond to in a positive way

I was so blessed to serendipitously cross paths with many such people. I was also blessed with enough personal support to be able to actively seek out these kind of people if I discovered they were absent in my professional support system. Thus, I have had the privilege of sharing this tribute with a wide variety of professionals in the biomedical, complementary, and spiritual care communities. While their specific gifts lie in vastly different areas, all with whom I have shared this poem possess the qualities I associate with true healers.

Those who assist me have a profound impact upon my healing.

Healer

Healer, pause now from your task -
You, who helps me when I ask -
Helps me find the Spirit's will,
Guides me with your care and skill.

Listen carefully to my words;
I wonder if they're often heard.
You go about your daily work
Without renown or extra perk.

Spirit sent you precious gifts;
Over trouble your work lifts
So I can, then, see my way clear
Through my dis-ease and dregs of fear.

Spirit guides you in your craft,
Creates a plan for you to draft;
Spirit guides me as I heal,
Teaching me what's right and real.

Spirit put you in my life
To help me heal from pain and strife.
I thank the Spirit every day
That you have come to share my way.

A fellow member of one of the two support groups I was attending asked me to write a poem for her because she was moving away. Having only known her for a short time, I was touched that she would wish me to have this privilege. I also found myself being concerned that I might not be able to find the words; it was the first time I had written something in response to a request.

I am very thankful for that request from a fellow traveler. First, it provided affirmation that the writing I had shared within the group actually could speak to others as well. Second, it provided me with the impetus to write about the precious circle of people in my support groups who have been so integral to my healing. Because of that request, I was given words to honour and celebrate the sacred circle of healing that can be found amongst fellow travelers. With her blessing, I now share those words.

I can find safety and healing amongst those who share my hurts.

Circle safe and so secure,
You bring me insights clear and sure;
You hold me in your loving arms;
You quell my angst and my alarm;

You bring me ways to find release,
To let things go, to find my peace;
You bring me lessons I must learn,
A winding wisdom that I yearn.

You bring me laughter and some fun
So there's a fresh perspective won,
And still, you let me shed a tear
If I feel sad or full of fear.

You bring me ones who've walked my way,
Who will support and love and pray,
Who understand what I must face,
Who listen with a special grace.

We share a very precious bond,
Convey a sense of care most fond,
Have high regard for one another -
No disrespect or will to smother.

And through these folk you bring me hope
And trust despite our steepened slope;
You bring me strength and new resolve
That I am free to still evolve.

And even when I leave your fold,
Your gifts inside I still will hold,
For they're the kind I'll take with me
Wherever I am meant to be.

I have participated in First Nations sweat lodges periodically throughout the course of my healing. I attended my first one just prior to chemotherapy. It assisted tremendously by helping me to cleanse and prepare physically, mentally, emotionally, and spiritually for the challenges ahead. For similar reasons, I also attended during and after my course of chemotherapy. By then, I also knew that sweat lodges are known to boost the immune system, something that I very much needed in the wake of a cancer diagnosis and chemotherapy. This information had been shared with me by one of the two elders who preside over the sweat lodges I attended. I am very grateful for her respectful attention to the needs of my Western-trained scientific mind by verbally sharing research identifying some specific benefits of this sacred ceremony. I am even more grateful for the way in which they have readily welcomed me into their community and shared their many gifts. In doing so, they have provided me with the opportunity to repeatedly experience a powerful sense of purification and inspiration that has strengthened and sustained me at all levels of my being.

My healing is a cycle of fresh beginnings.

Sweat Lodge

Sweat Lodge, Sweat Lodge, dark and safe,
Please take in this wandering waif;
Hold me close so I can pray,
That I may walk the Spirit's way.

Cradle me within your womb;
Nestle all who share this room
'Midst the gifts of Mother Earth;
Prepare us for a bright rebirth.

Wrapped up tight in your cocoon,
I sing with all a soothing tune;
I learn about Creator's way
Before I see the light of day.

Cleanse me with your Spirit Steam
Until my soul and body gleam
With pearls of sweat and sacrifice
That open me, new growth entice.

When I crawl out your Sacred Door
I spread my wings so I can soar,
Ready for a whole new life,
Prepared to meet both joy and strife.

I share good food, refreshing drink
With all who share this Sacred link;
I thank Creator for this Sweat
And all the blessed people met.

Sweat Lodge, Sweat Lodge, safe and dark,
You have left the Spirit's mark
Deep within my humble heart,
Preparing me for this new start.

Many of the healing practices I have been blessed to experience are 'energy-based'; that is, they focus on assisting individuals to attain a smooth flow of energy throughout the body, facilitating balance, and, in turn, promoting healing. Such modalities include therapeutic and healing touch, Reiki, accupressure, reflexology, yoga, and various types of meditative activity. While these practices have emerged from different parts of the world, their conceptualization of energy flow is remarkably similar (Myss, 1997; Northrup, 1998). I have been increasingly amazed by the universality of this understanding as I have experienced a variety of modalities and gained my own understanding of them, of my body, and, indeed, of my entire Being. This personal, intuitive understanding has been validated by contemporary scientific theory (Chopra, 1990; Wager, 1996).

As my understanding has evolved, I have also found myself in ever-growing awe of how the intangible we call 'energy' truly connects and influences every realm of our Being. The healing systems I have encountered not only have offered me a deeper level of understanding, but a way to *experience* the 'mind/body/spirit connection' we hear so much about these days. Many times, I have *felt* this connection in very concrete ways. As I began to write about my experience with breast cancer, I literally experienced a clearing in my throat and chest area, releasing congestion throughout the entire initial period when the floodgates were opening and my voice was being freed. Often, I experience 'tingles' and other physical sensations in all areas of my body when I am being assisted with 'energy' or 'body' work or when I visualize the universally-identified colours along the prism that are associated with each energy centre or 'chakra' radiating throughout, above, below, and around me. 'Rainbow' honours my vision and experience of this energy. As these physical manifestations of its presence began occurring I became aware that my process of healing was evolving. I was not only connecting with my head through imagery and visualization, but with my heart and gut in opening my voice and my body to this amazing expression of Spirit. While I was once a skeptic, I have come to believe its Universality and its Power to be nothing less than this - a sacred expression of Spirit.

Spirit flows through me.

Rainbow

Rainbow Column
Through my Core
And Around,
Where Body, Mind and Soul
Are One,
Where Head, Heart and Gut
Connect,
Extend endlessly into
The Earth below
And the Heavens above,
Drawing Light
That opens and heals
And fills me
With Rainbow Promise.

Early mornings have always been a very significant time of day for me. I have often been visited by powerful dream experiences in these hours, particularly in the past couple of years. It seems to be the time of day at which I am most in touch with my emotional and spiritual state. During my illness and healing, this has made for some intense awakenings!

This poem was written during a time period of exquisite joy and creativity that lasted for weeks after that pivotal Easter. It chronicles the incredible transition from despair to joy that had gradually occurred for me as creativity was becoming my voice and my healer. I believe this amazing process to be a miracle unfolding as I journeyed 'on toward morning' out of the darkness that had enveloped me.

Miracles do happen.

On Toward Morning

I used to awake,
Awash with such terror
I just couldn't shake,
Thinking of all that
We still had at stake,
So knotted in fear;
My whole being would ache.

I would dread waking up
To a hopeless, dark dawn;
To just be reminded
Our problems weren't gone;
I'd only get scared
That more trouble would spawn;
I'd wonder if I
Could still carry on.

I could not alone -
That was one thing for sure.
I needed some Spirit
To keep me secure,
That could chase away doubt
So despair couldn't lure,
That could fill me with peace
And a Presence so pure.

But I just couldn't find Her;
She seemed far away.
I hadn't the focus
To journal or pray;
Day in and day out
I'd continue to stray,
Convinced that I simply
Could not find my way.

'Til, finally, I could not
Stay lost anymore;
There was too much inside
I no longer could store;
So, I'd wake up and head
Out of my bedroom door -
And onto blank pages
My troubles would pour.

It took weeks and weeks
'Til my mornings came 'round,
'Til my wanderings ceased
And my Helper was found.
On those ragged pages
Release would abound;
The healing within them
Began to astound.

Now, on toward morning
I often awake
With insights and plans
That I can't wait to make.
My Angels come by,
Whispering words for my sake;
They rouse me so gently
Just at the daybreak.

Seems Spirit has sent them
To this sleepy space
To affirm and renew,
Bring peace to this place.
Receptive and calm,
Our wills interlace,
Prepared for the day
I'm about to embrace.

So, on toward morning
I hale the new day!
I can't wait to witness
What it brings my way!
I can't wait to say
Everything I must say!
I can't wait to live,
To explore, and to play!

On toward morning!!
I now celebrate
The dawn of a new life -
A marvelous state!
Each morning I wake up
And walk through the gate
Of Discovery and Wonder,
Unfolding my Fate!

As I began to experience the consummate joy of that spring, I knew it was finally time to return a symbol lent to me by a close friend almost a year before. She had brought it to me in the hospital and pinned it on my housecoat. *Triumph Over Tragedy* tells the rest of the story surrounding this powerful symbol.

I was blessed with many symbolic gifts and gestures which provided me with much inspiration. Many such symbols decorated my room at the hospital. Many later adorned my home, particularly my kitchen bulletin board where I could be reminded of their messages amidst the trappings of everyday schedules and routines. I am so grateful to those who employed such creativity and thoughtfulness to demonstrate their caring.

Symbols carry phenomenal healing power.

Triumph Over Tragedy

My dear friend, you have seen me through
The trials of Tragedy;
The time is right to celebrate -
Triumph has come to be!

It now is time that I returned
The symbol you gave me,
A golden pin with faces bold -
Triumph and Tragedy.

You shared this very special gift
When Tragedy had reign
And told me I could keep it close
'Til Triumph came again!

Your pin's two faces cry and laugh,
Reminding me I could
Find both releases on the way -
That find the way, I would.

So, now that Triumph reigns again,
It's time to pass it on
To someone else who needs some hope
When all their hope is gone.

Its image bright remains within:
Life's laughter and its tears.
I'm here to share them both with you
For many more long years!

This ecstatic little piece is yet another expression of the sheer 'joie de vive' in which I reveled that spring! I took nothing for granted and experienced life more fully than I had ever been able to before.

***When I am paying attention, it is the smallest things that bring me
the biggest joy.***

The Little Things

Now I treasure little things
Throughout my every day;
I notice them and bright bells ring -
"Rejoice!" they seem to say.

When I had lost my old routine,
A new one I attained;
I saw things I had never seen;
Wise wonderment I gained!

It feels so good to just feel good,
To do my own dear tasks,
To laugh and love, do what I would,
To hide behind no masks.

For I no longer sacrifice
One part of my bright day;
Indifference is too high a price
To ever have to pay.

It wastes the very precious time
We're given on this earth;
It keeps our bells from their full chime,
From ringing out their mirth.

For hugs and mugs and pretty rugs,
For everything I see,
For pugs and jugs and tiny bugs
My bells toll happily!

For friends, fajitas, and good fun
For all that comes to me
My bells ring out and celebrate!
True joy has come to be!

Yes! I treasure little things
Throughout my ev'ry day!
I honour them - and bright bells ring -
"Rejoice!" they surely say!

The tree honoured here has been a symbol central to my imagery work throughout my healing. Initially, it represented my immune and energy systems outgrowing and outshining any unwanted elements within me. Later on, it became a very grounding symbol of my will to live, grow and flourish according to my Creator's will. As I wrote this poem, the tree became a symbol of the transformation and renewal I was experiencing that spring.

Thanks to my brother-in-law's inspiration to add a refrain to *Tree of Life*, a tune also accompanied this creation - the first of many tunes to follow. This delightful surprise occurred just in time for it to be shared in song form at a special occasion for a close friend. I was delighted that this had happened because the tree has long been a powerful symbol for her, for a variety of reasons. Furthermore, having both experienced a very difficult year it was wonderful to be at a point of celebration together. Indeed, our *Tree of Life* was abundantly flourishing.

When my parents later heard this song sung by friends in our church, the tree became, for them, a symbol of faith and rejuvenation. It seems the same symbol can speak to many different people in many different ways.

Life is irrepressible.

Tree of Life

My Tree of Life stands firm and tall,
Deep-rooted in the earth;
She reaches up toward the heavens,
Her being filled with mirth.

She sports abundant foliage
So full and rich and green
That soaks up Universal Light
From Energies unseen.

She's also thick with blossoms
So pure and fresh and white
That cleanse, renew and celebrate
A Transformation rite.

You see, my tree's been through a storm
Of thunder, wind and rain
That's flushed out all that's old and dead
And christened her with pain.

My tree has weathered pretty well
That unexpected gale.
She's sprung new growth at every twig.
Bright days she now can hail!

She's stronger now, more flexible
Since she has had this test.
No matter what new weather comes,
She trusts it brings what's best.

And even when I'm old and gone,
My vessel in the ground,
My Tree of Life lives on and on -
Life just goes 'round and 'round.

Tree of Life, Oh, Tree of Life!
Reach up into the Light!
And let the healing touch of God
Bring you to your full height!

As the name of my publishing company reflects, the image of myself as a granny is a very precious and prominent one for me in my visualizations to help keep mind, body, and spirit focused on well-being. In fact, a 'granny' image has been central to a couple of my powerful dream experiences. Often she comes to me as my Inner Guide, also representing my 'higher self' whom I strive to become.

I see myself becoming more like her every day. I see myself growing old - something I will never complain about! I've been too close to the alternative; growing old will be an honour and a privilege.

With my Creator's guidance, I am becoming all that I am intended to be.

Granny Me...

Wise old eyes
And a loving face,
Strengthening arms
That reach to embrace;
Silver waves -
Rolling wild
Like the sea -
That had surfaced anew
To crown a new me.

Work-worn hands
That have learned how to give
And to take what is offered -
A fine balance to live;
Light-stepping feet
That have learned how to dance
And to follow the Spirit,
Her journey enhance.

Laughing, calm heart
And disciplined mind -
Both have learned to leave hurts
Of the past behind;
A flexible body
That knows what it's beat,
That knows it can weather
New storms it may meet.

And hidden from most
Are the scars that have saved,
Have afforded new healing,
A new road have paved -
A small price to pay
For new life and new voice,
New views and relations
To daily rejoice.

A powerful lady
From head to her toes
Who loves life and living,
Wherever it goes.
Her Spirit grows stronger
With each passing day
'Til It parts from her body
And goes soaring away.

I wish I could say that I always maintain the rhythm I had found at the joyous time during which I wrote this poem. Still, there are many more days than not when I now am able to find such balance. These days occur when I remember that my Internal Rhythm has far more wisdom than do the competing routines of my own and others' making. Rhythmic days also occur when I remember that following this Rhythm is good not only for me but for those around me; when I am harmonious I influence everyone and everything with whom I come in contact.

These realizations are teaching me it is central to my well-being to listen to my Internal Rhythm rather than to focus only on meeting external expectations as I have tended to do in the past.

When I follow my Internal Rhythm I am carrying out a Divine plan for my day.

Rhythm

A Rhythm's come into my life.
In an unexpected way.
I need not hurry anymore
Nor worry through my day.

This Rhythm gently guides me
To all things that are good.
It leads me and prevents me from
Just doing things I "should".

It encompasses a little
Of all life has to give:
Some work, some play, some time to pray -
It shows me how to live!

It teaches me to balance
And let my angst release.
It brings to me a harmony
That fosters inner peace.

It soothes me like good poetry
With elements that lull;
It sends me rays of insight
So life is never dull!

It's shown to me that I just can't
Please others all the time.
I have to please myself instead -
My own Rhythm is prime.

And, too, I'm learning give and take
Are both necessities;
I can't give from an empty cup -
So, fill my cup up, please!

A Rhythm's come into my life
To show me a new way.
It helps me fill and share my cup
And handle 'come what may'!

Around the time this poem was created, I made a commitment to stop
referring to myself as a perfectionist. While I need to acknowledge that this
tendency within me is still strong, I do not wish to perpetuate a self-
fulfilling prophecy that reinforces destructive old habits and drains me of
energy. So, now I simply say: "I have a *background* in perfectionism!"

The best reinforcement for letting my perfectionism 'lapse' has been the
repeated occurrence of blessings that I could never have previously
envisioned, much less engineered or managed. The evolution of this book is
the most dramatic and recent example. I come back to this poem when I
start taking myself too seriously and thinking that it is all up to me to make
everything happen as it 'should'. I also re-read it if I begin to feel terrified
by the lack of control I have over so many things. It reminds me that I can
be freed, rather than terrified, by not being 'in charge'.

I can find freedom in letting go.

Manager

I used to be a manager
When things were pretty good;
I'd plan and work and organize
And do more than I should;

But life brought some surprises
That threw me for a loop!
I couldn't steer nor manage -
Control began to droop.

I kept on trying my old tricks,
But they just wouldn't work;
I was trying to run the Universe,
Conform it to MY quirk.

So finally I declared defeat;
I had to let things go -
Began to let uncertainty
Sway me to and fro.

Lo and behold! I liked the ride
And trust I did befriend.
Along came flexibility
And I began to bend.

The really, truly wondrous thing
Is that's when things improved;
The roadblock of my ego
Was finally removed!

What a relief to not be "chief" -
Life flows all on its own.
Someone Else is Manager -
I don't do it alone!

It was a mixed blessing to be gaining many insights around the same time. My fresh perspective on the importance of 'letting go' and pacing myself was difficult to balance with my growing desire to live my life to the fullest. A heightened awareness of my mortality seemed to have brought these two intents into some sort of cruel and confusing competition with one another. At the same time that I was trying to learn to listen consistently to my internal rhythm and give up my illusion of control I was determined not to slip back into a mundane existence. Hence, I was intent on trying many new things - things which were both physically demanding and, at times, anxiety-producing to learn. As terrified of life becoming ordinary and routine as I was of it running out on me, I drove myself to partake in these activities despite the fact I had not yet even regained my usual stamina. In addition, I had just finished my first two months of full-time work and I was exhausted.

This poem was written during a camping/canoeing trip that I almost allowed to be ruined by the resulting angst and inner conflict. I was grateful to find the words for *Urgency* as I sat by the lake early one morning. Being able to do so helped me begin to sort through the conflicts and to be able to express them more clearly to my husband and my sister-in-law (who is also a dear friend and the one who witnessed most closely my angst that weekend). This release not only salvaged the excursion, but brought some beginning clarity about what I needed to do. (It also nicely watered the foliage around our campsite with an abundance of tears!)

This poem was particularly significant for me in that it was the first one (aside from *Images*) that I had been able to write in the midst of a painful time. This was the beginning of my being able to find words for my experience and thus create in the moment, rather than weeks or months afterward. Perhaps the backlog was finally clearing. In any case, it was clearly a turning point on the journey.

Experiencing each moment is all I need to do.

Urgency

Just when I need to let things go
I feel pressure to include
All the things I have not done -
With no healing interlude.

I wonder if there will be time
To try things I have not -
To live my life the way I want,
Fulfill the dreams I've sought.

I wonder if I wait too long -
Will I lose this brave new spark?
Harbored where it's safe and sure,
Will I never, then, embark?

I wonder why it took so long
To want these things so much
And now, this late, adventure may
Elude my desperate clutch.

I wish I had embraced it all
When I felt less urgency -
When risks and thrilling challenges
Could be paced and more care-free.

For even though I seek new joys,
It's hard to learn new things.
I cannot do it all at once -
No matter what life brings.

Perhaps therein is what I need
To release this urgency -
To know that I just cannot rush
If joy is going to be.

Perhaps I am a lucky one
Who's discovered when there's time
That life won't last forever -
That this moment must be prime.

So I won't waste this moment
Feeling pressure or regret.
Instead, I will be ready,
For the best of living yet.

I'll be set to grasp with passion
Each opportunity -
And let each moment teach me how
To live abundantly.

The sense of urgency I struggled with acutely for a considerable time was clearly rooted in fear. While I continued to carry within me many images of longevity and health, I could not deny I was still terrified they would not come true. In fact, I believe I was truly just beginning to accept that I had even had a diagnosis of cancer and that this reality was not about to go away. There were times when I would still wake up in the morning and feel a rush of terror and profound disappointment that this disease had actually become a part of my life. These feelings would quickly be followed by fresh anger that I had to learn to live with this fact. Close on its heels would be guilt that I didn't feel more grateful just to be alive.

I had been told it takes at least two years to fully accept a cancer diagnosis and incorporate its presence into one's self-image and life. This wisdom had been shared by ones who would know, the long-term cancer survivors from HOPE Vancouver who facilitated a retreat I had attended for women dealing with cancer. Still, it surprised me to again be struggling emotionally after thinking only a few weeks earlier that I 'had it all together'.

A part of me figured it couldn't possibly take me that long to come to terms with everything that had happened, especially when I had been given so much support by so many. I cannot imagine what my reaction would have been without that support or without the wisdom of the retreat facilitators.

I believe the most perplexing irony for me to accept was that the desire to fully live in the moment, awakened by having experienced a threat to my life, was so very difficult to fulfill *because* of that very threat. *Of course* it was going to take time to learn to wield this colossal double-edged sword.

I am learning to accept the shadows in my life.

Shadow

I have this lingering shadow
That now comes along with me;
It's an escort on my journey;
That's how it's going to be.

There's no use in pretending
That it just isn't there;
Its looming greyness grips me
In worry and despair.

Sometimes, I can forget it -
But, most times, not at all -
For when I turn, it's there again
And terror comes to call.

At times, I find contentment
With this new, unwelcome friend
If I accept its presence
And face the sun ahead.

For, then, it stays behind me
And I walk along, more free.
And though I know it follows,
It's sun, not shade, I see.

At those times, this companion
Is a blessing rare and strange;
Its presence oft reminds me
That some things I can't change.

I cannot look behind me
If I'm to move ahead
With courage and conviction
Instead of fear and dread.

The darkness of this shadow
Then makes the rest seem light;
The world, in contrast, sparkles,
Its details crisp and bright.

So I won't fight my shadow,
Resist its stealthy gloom
And I won't let its darkness
Envelope and consume.

I will walk into the sunshine
And it will come behind -
It's truly just a shadow -
This moment's Light I'll find.

As I wrestled with the ongoing issues and challenges associated with incorporating the reality of cancer into my life, my spirits again plummeted. I was devastated not only by tumbling down off my 'mountain-top' experience of that spring but by the sense that I seemed to be regressing, rather than progressing in terms of my growth and healing. Just at the time when I needed inspiration to resume my routine roles and responsibilities it seemed I was grieving all over again, finding myself consumed with sadness and worry I thought I had left behind. My anguish was compounded by a growing fear of how this escalating discord might be impacting upon my physical well-being, knowing that stress is a known suppressant of the immune system, my best protector against cancer. I was able to do none of the exciting things I had planned to do over that summer - simply because I didn't feel like it. My disappointment was profound.

All of these emotional experiences were compounded by the physical and emotional exhaustion associated with side effects from the adjuvent medication I was on at the time. Because I believed I needed the medication to prevent a recurrence, I was as terrified to go off it as I was to remain on it.

To add salt to the wound, my celebrated curls were definitely disappearing. The return of my characteristically straight hair, to me, symbolized the return of the ordinary I was finding so very hard to take. It also seemed to confirm that I had lost touch with that elusive 'new me'. (Clearly, the image of myself as a granny with beautiful silver waves was going to need re-creation!) It seemed so trivial to grieve this minor change in my body image, but grieve it I did. It had been so much easier to be brave with those wild new curls on my head!

The valleys are as much a part of the healing as are the mountain-tops.

Let Down

Curls of joy have gone away.
Let down, loosening locks now lay.
Are new beginnings gone astray?
The ordinary here to stay?

Trivial trappings enter in
Where sure serenity had been.
To lose it now seems such a sin.
Are old entrapments going to win?

Wondering if I've learned a thing,
I question what this dip will bring.
Will new awareness yet take wing
In this, the autumn of my spring?

Knowing well that seasons change,
Indeed, I must accept their range.
This sudden shifting still seems strange.
My expectations rearrange.

Tempered Wisdom, please emerge
More lasting than my springtime surge.
It seems I must abide this dirge
To truly let my sadness purge.

Sadness for what's gone before,
That jubilation is no more,
That mundane matters inward pour,
And routine life comes to the fore.

Sadness that I now must find
A way to leave my fear behind,
To keep a peaceful state of mind
Amidst the daily tasks that bind.

'Twas easy in a joyful state
To trust life to unfold my fate.
With curls of joy all now gone straight
It is so hard to watch and wait.

When I trust 'midst dreary days
I'll know I've learned the Spirit's ways.
For now, I must endure this phase.
Prayers for healing now I raise.

As I contended with and reflected upon the challenges I continued to face, I found myself overwhelmed at times by the incredible depth and range of feelings I had experienced over the course of my journey thus far. I began to wonder if I also had to learn to live with a permanently and dramatically heightened level of sensitivity - a sensitivity I could do without. I had possessed enough of it before - I certainly didn't need this burden on top of everything else. How was I supposed to find serenity and healing amidst such tumult?!

Slowly, I began to remember my earlier lessons and to consider that, perhaps, serenity comes in learning to fully experience the passage through all of those valleys and mountains of emotion - trusting that I am being guided by a wise and loving Navigator. In, once again, giving in to the whimsical nature of healing, maybe I could find the courage to feel - to vent - to process - and to learn from those exquisitely intense emotions. As one friend said, "They must be there for a reason." She was right because they have, eventually, guided me to do more of the things I need to do - things like saying what needs to be said, meeting needs that need to be met, and living in the way I wish to live. I simply can no longer ignore the intensity of their message - and increasingly, I am finding that when I listen to their message, they dissipate.

Gradually, the vast extremes have decreased, perhaps signaling that I am healing as I need to. Somehow, I think some of that intensity will always remain. That may not be a bad thing - IF I KEEP LISTENING.

Spirit speaks to me through my emotions.

Spirit Storm

Spirit Guide, you've come to me
In dream, in verse, in deed,
And still, it is so hard to trust
That I'll find what I need.

Spirits soar, then spirits dip,
I swing from faith to fear;
I find you, live you, lose you and
Then wonder if you're here.

My courage waxes, then it wanes
To trembling all time lows.
My sense of peace and harmony
Forever comes and goes.

Joy so bright, despair so dark,
Intensity the norm -
The only constant I can see
Amidst this Spirit Storm.

Spirit Guide, I want to know
Will I now always feel
Extremes of passion in all things?
Is there an even keel?

Invincible, then vulnerable -
It may be these extremes
Are teaching me I must be both
To follow Spirit Schemes.

Spirit Guide, please show me how
These wild extremes can meet
That I may learn, no matter what,
I will not know defeat.

It was becoming clear to me by this point that maintaining the serenity so central to fostering the healing process was going to be a difficult and ongoing challenge.

Spirit and its accompanying tune has become a very soothing invocation that helps keep me open to the Creator's presence and guidance.

I am not alone.

Spirit

Spirit, come and share my way.
Stay beside me every day.
Please be with me when I pray
And in everything I do.

Help me learn to let You lead.
Let You teach me what I need.
Come, inspire my every deed
And bring me harmony.

Help me cleanse and to renew.
Bring me a fresh point of view.
Fill me with a trust that's true
And help my faith grow strong.

As everyday life slowly resumed, I was still haunted by the fear that I would make the wrong choices about my health care and family, personal, work and volunteer commitments - choices that might be detrimental to my health and happiness. After having had a huge 'wake-up call' in my life, I expected that I should know clearly and immediately what I needed to clear out of my life and what I needed to bring into it. With my 'background in perfectionism' it was easy to believe that somehow my life needed to be perfect in order for me to find healing. After all, it hadn't been perfect before - and look what happened?!

Here was another lesson in 'letting go'. The pressure within myself to turn on a dime (when I didn't even know where or if I needed to turn!) became too great. I could sense that this pressure was likely more unhealthy for me than remaining on a 'wrong' or divergent path for a period of time. It was at this point of 'letting go' that I began to realize I was not in a space to be making major decisions; not only was I unsure of what I wanted, I had had enough change and upheaval. I began to recognize that I simply was not ready for more change right then, even if it was 'constructive'.

It was not long afterward that some wonderful surprises began to surface. First, a series of events led me to incredible clarity that it was time to abandon the medication that was causing me so much grief. Not only did I begin to feel better within days, I felt safe and confident in my decision. As I began to experience many unexpected new joys in my work and family life, I began to find this inexplicable contentment and acceptance of my circumstances, knowing that I would do what I needed to do in good time.

The exploration and wonderings have since resumed, but in an unhurried, contented way, just as I had tried to affirm would happen when I wrote *Belonging*.

I will be guided in my choices.

Be-longing...

Sorting out what goes, what stays,
Believing I must change some ways
To let my healing rise.

I know I need not change it all.
Yet, that is where I hit a wall —
I don't know what belongs.

Daily challenges still come.
How will I ever tell these from
The things I must let go?

I've lost my faith in my instinct,
In how my health and life are linked.
I thought I knew before.

Now, I question every move.
What if I just miss the groove?
Will healing pass me by?

It seems that only time can tell
What I'm to keep, what I'm to quell;
I cannot know today.

So I will listen with my heart
And let my brooding fears depart;
Then peace can settle in.

For only peace can help me heal
And help me find what's right and real
So choices will be wise.

And, too, such peace serves to remind
That circumstances do not bind.
Responses to them do.

It may be that's where shifts will be -
Not in my world, but within me -
From inside change will come.

Wisdom, then, can ripple out.
Clarity will come about ...
And I'll know what belongs.

As a renewed sense of peace is settling into my life, I am able to see the tumult I experienced following my initial period of delirious joy as a necessary part of my journey. Primarily, it has finally taught me this journey will never really finish. There will be no miraculous, permanent transformation, no jubilant victory, no fairy tale happy ending. Instead, there will be ongoing challenges, an ever-heightened level of awareness, a continuing intensity of emotion, and an ever-expanding ability to find serenity in the present moment. Somehow, I'm not sorry.

My joy lies in the never-ending journey.

Spiral Path

I'm ever on a spiral path
That circles up and 'round
And every time I make a turn
I'm reaching higher ground.

I move along my spiral path,
My progress fast or slow.
I sometimes long for, sometimes fear
The places I must go.

I sometimes run along my path,
Anticipation stokes
The fitful fires of my power,
My courage it evokes.

I sometimes crawl along my path,
Exhausted or afraid,
My power dwindling for a time
As Spirit's plans are laid.

At times, I halt there on my path,
Unsure of what's ahead,
Aware of blockades in and out,
Immobilized by dread.

More often now I walk my path.
An even, steady pace
Allows me to move on and yet
To know this moment's grace.

For whether there are obstacles
Or clear road on my way
I cannot rush nor can I stall,
Lest I should go astray.

For every blockade that I clear
And every moment lived
Frees me to be so much more
And shows me how to give.

And yet, I must remember all
The places on the way
Where I can sit and rest awhile,
Receive all that I may.

For only then will I be fit
To see my journey through,
To find out what's in store for me
And what I'm meant to do.

I'm ever on a spiral path
That circles up and 'round
And every time I make a turn
I'm reaching higher ground.

The serenity I am gradually regaining in my everyday life cannot be separated from the serenity I am finding with regard to my personal healing. It is as though I am coming to the end of a long detour on which I have had the opportunity to explore and participate in a variety of healing experiences - as though I am now returning to a main pathway with an expanded awareness of a few simple things I need to take with me on the next leg of my journey.

I am as inconsistent as anyone in my ability to apply what I have learned. However, I have come to know that I feel best when each day, I find my own unique way to do five basic things:

- cleanse physically, emotionally, mentally and spiritually
- help my immune system to stay strong
- clear energy blocks and prevent new ones from forming
- keep my body well energized with quality diet, rest and exercise
- trust

The latter is pivotal, not because I believe that 'positive thinking' or 'faith' controls what happens to me, but because I believe the serenity that comes with trust allows my body and my entire being to heal at its optimum. It also affords me a quality of life I have not experienced before, impacting positively on every aspect of my health and my living.

I believe I could not have come to these basic insights without taking that long detour on which I encountered and experienced a number of resources, healers, and modalities from a variety of healing systems. However, it has been learning to listen to my own Intuition - that which connects me to my Creator - which has enabled me to recognize the simple truths I need to embrace as I continue on.

While others' insights inform me, it is my own Wisdom that guides me to my Truth.

I NEED

To create
And to be re-created

To be heard
And to listen

To dream
And to be grounded

To dance
And to plod

To laugh
And to cry

To soar
And to land

To sing
And to whisper

To be fed
And be cleansed

To stretch
And to walk

To rest
And to toil

To hug
And be hugged

To ask
And to answer

To lead
To follow

To open
To close

To say hello
And to say good bye

To celebrate life
And to honour death

To do

TO BE

Environmental pollution is one factor in the development of cancer and many other illnesses that is becoming more and more apparent; several elements and circumstances in our ecosystem are known contributors (Colborn et al, 1996). While many cultural and individual factors also have been linked to such manifestations, it is clear that today's environment, in general, is putting all of us at higher risk to experience disruptions in our health (Colborn et al, 1996).

I'm not sure if knowledge of this reality has made me feel better or worse. My initial response to such information is often a strange sense of relief that this illness wasn't 'all my own fault' in relation to lifestyle choices or ways of being. The temptation is to absolve myself of any responsibility for a disease and situation I don't control. Then, I find myself becoming angry - *again - SO VERY, VERY ANGRY* - that things have spun *so far* out of control as we have sought to control our natural world for our convenience - that I simply cannot, as my husband says, go back to the 1800s in terms of lifestyle - that others don't do something about this mess - that people like me who already have to focus on personal survival also have to concern ourselves with global survival. But, then, I have to ask myself - isn't that the struggle for all of us? Isn't it just that, often, we fail to acknowledge that struggle until our own well-being or that of a loved one is threatened - and it all becomes too real to us?

It's true that none of us can heal this earth alone. However, perhaps those of us who have been touched by the poison of today's toxic world need to lead the way. As unfair as that may seem, I don't see any other way. The challenge becomes balancing our need for personal healing with the demands of global healing. Or, are they one and the same?

My healing expands to encompass my family, my community and my world.

What Is Healing, Anyway? ...

Finding Voice
Vibrant and strong;
Cleansing All,
Joining the throng;
Trusting One
Much wiser than we
To transform
The world and me!

If we heard the Earth speak,what would She say?
We are Her voice! What do *we* say?!
"Don't block, don't choke, don't silence me!
Give me time and space to rest, to BE!
Replenish me with purity
That I may give abundantly!"

For how are we to heal without each other?
She needs us and we need her!
"Restore Her sacred tapestry
That's woven right through you and me,
Connecting All creatively
That we may live abundantly!"

Finding Voice,
Vibrant and strong;
Cleansing All,
Joining the throng;
Trusting One
Much wiser than we
To transform
The world and me!

As the focus of my healing has broadened I have discovered a need within me to step back from many of the formal support systems I earlier relied upon. A short time ago I could not have envisioned surviving - much less thriving - without them. Yet now, it seems maintaining all these involvements would only impede my ability to continue healing and living my life the way I want. Just as I could not have come thus far without these supports, I cannot carry on without saying good-bye to some of them so that I can make room in my life for new Connections that allow my healing to begin to ripple outward.

I know without a doubt there are no guarantees; as one of my support people has said, "It can all be taken away from any one of us tomorrow." I must be making peace with this reality because it has now become precisely the reason I want to live for today. The delightful paradox is that in doing so, I am finding healing at all levels of my being.

Life is today.

It is time to move on,

To align with life and health,

Not a disease I had yesterday

And may never have tomorrow.

Yes, I will die

Tomorrow or in fifty years

Or somewhere in-between.

Today I will live.

Afterword

It is clear by now the story does not end here. There is much more I could write, but at this point, it would be little more than continued, but more rapid repetitions of the same discoveries over and over again - discoveries that allow me to keep arriving back at a point where I can live fully in the moment, thus contributing to my own and my world's healing. Each time I return, I'm a little better at doing just that. (A friend and I quipped one day over lunch that if there *were* any more to be written now, a directive such as the following would suffice: *"See pages 'such and such' to 'such and such' ... again... and again... and again...'!!!*)

Sometimes, I truly feel like I am going around and around the same circle. Then, I recall the truth I found in the images of *Spirit Spiral* and *Spiral Path* - and I know I *am* still healing and evolving - in Time ... in Cycles ... in Spirals. Sometimes those Spirals are so very tightly coiled it is difficult to detect any upward movement. Sometimes they escalate so very freely and openly there is no doubt I am moving on, and, somehow, being readied for new challenges up ahead. In any case, the images I have found on these pages affirm that my Process is, indeed, being guided...

And, once again, ... I am overwhelmed by the Grace and Wisdom of Spirit.

Sources of Learning...

Bolen, Jean Shinoda. (1996). *Close to the Bone: Life-Threatening Illness and the Search for Meaning*. New York: Scribner

Carkhuff, Robert R. (1993). *The Art of Helping*. 7th Edition. Amherst, Mass.: Human Resources Development Press.

Chopra, Deepak. (1990). *Quantum Healing: Exploring the Frontiers of Body, Mind, Medicine*. Toronto: Bantam Books.

Colborn, T., Dumonoski, D. & Peterson Meyers, J. (1996). *Our Stolen Future: A Scientific Detective Story*. New York: Dutton.

Egan, Gerard. (1998). *The Skilled Helper*. 6th Edition. Scarborough, Ont.: Nelson Canada.

Fenwick, Catherine Ripplinger. (1995). *Healing With Humour: A Laughter First-Aid Kit*. Muenster, Sask.: St. Peter's Press.

Kreiger, Delores. (1993). *Accepting Your Power to Heal: The Personal Practice of Therapeutic Touch*. Santa Fe, New Mexico: Bear & Co.

Lorde, Audre. (1984). *Sister Outsider: Essays and Speeches*. Trumansberg, NY: Crossing Press.

Milne, Courtney & Miller, Sherrill. (1998). *Visions of the Goddess*. Toronto: Penguin Books.

Myss, Caroline. (1996). *Anatomy of the Spirit*. New York: Three Rivers Press, Crown Publishers.

Northrup, Christiane. (1998). *Women's Bodies, Women's Wisdom: Creating Physical and Emotional Health and Healing.* Toronto: Bantam Books.

Nursing Education Program of Saskatchewan. (1999). *Curriculum Documents.* Saskatchewan Institute of Applied Science and Technology/University of Saskatchewan.

Paape, Valerie. (1996). Guilt as a Chronic Illness. *Herizons (10)2,* p.40.

Pert, Candace B. (1997). *Molecules of Emotion.* New York: Scribner.

Quinn, Janet. (1996). Therapeutic Touch and the Healing Way: Janet Quinn R.N. Phd. [Interview by Bonnie Horrigan]. *Alternative Therapies in Health and Medicine (2)4,* pp.62-75.

Remen, Naomi Rachel. (1996). *Kitchen Table Wisdom.* New York: Riverhead Books.

Tafoya, Terry. (1997). Every Tragedy Comes With A Gift In Hand. *Bridging The Gaps: Communication and Continuity of Care.* Saskatoon, Sask. The Canadian Association of Psychosocial Oncology Annual Meeting and Conference, May 28-30, 1997.

Wager, Susan. (1996). *A Doctor's Guide to Therapeutic Touch.* New York: Berkley Publishing Group.

Wilkes, James. (1993). *To Wrestle and to Dance: Reflections on the Power of Faith.* Toronto: Penguin Books.

Photo by John Stusek

About the author ...

Karen Scott Barss is a Registered Psychiatric Nurse (RPN), a Nurse Educator at the Saskatchewan Institute of Applied Science and Technology (SIAST), a Certified Reflexologist, and a breast cancer survivor. She has written and presented on the topic of healing from a personal and professional perspective in a variety of forums. Born and raised in Indian Head, Saskatchewan, she lives in Saskatoon, Saskatchewan, with her husband, two sons, and their faithful canine friend, Clover.

TO ORDER COPIES OF THIS BOOK COMPLETE THE ORDER FORM BELOW:

Please send _____ copies of *Healing Images* @ $16.00 each (GST included) $ _____

Add $4.00 postage & handling per book $ _____

Total $ _____

Name: _____

Address: _____

Town/City: _____ Province: _____ Postal Code: _____

Phone: _____ Fax: _____ Email _____

Enclose cheque or money order payable to:

The Granny Ranch Publishing House

Box 23026-2325 Preston Ave.

Saskatoon, Sask. S7J 5H3   email: kms.barss@sk.sympatico.ca

Books are available at special discounts on bulk orders
for bookstores, fund raising or educational use.
Please email for pricing on bulk or international orders.

Please send _____ copies of *Healing Images* @ $16.00 each (GST included) $ _____

Add $4.00 postage & handling per book $ _____

Total $ _____

Name: _____

Address: _____

Town/City: _____ Province: _____ Postal Code: _____

Phone: _____ Fax: _____ Email _____

Enclose cheque or money order payable to:

The Granny Ranch Publishing House

Box 23026-2325 Preston Ave.

Saskatoon, Sask. S7J 5H3   email: kms.barss@sk.sympatico.ca

Books are available at special discounts on bulk orders
for bookstores, fund raising or educational use.
Please email for pricing on bulk or international orders.

NOTE: Prints featuring a specific *Healing Images* poem can be special-ordered.
Please inquire at above address or email.